Dynamics of Qigong Healing

Dynamics of Qigong Healing

Meridian Healing
Level I Course

Chok C. Hiew
&
Yap SoonYeong

BookSurge
Publishing

Dynamics of Qigong Healing
Meridian Healing: A CFQ Level I Course

First published: 2001
Revised 2005

ISBN: 0-9730387-2-1

Printed in Canada

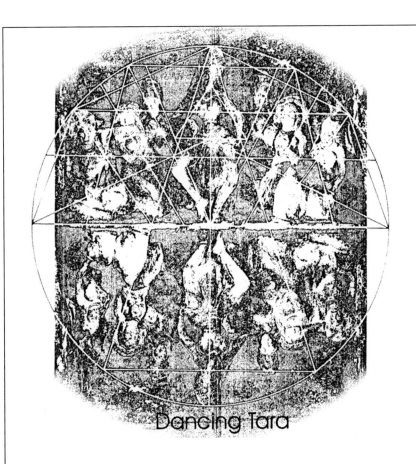

Dancing Tara

Dedicated to the Timeless Traveler

May your journeys since Creation
Between the two Eternities
Be in perpetual motion flowing Homeward with
Resilience, Peace, and Boundless Love

Contents

List of Illustrations and Figures

Meridian Exercises:
7-Step Hexagram Dance

List of Illustrations and Figures

Meridian Techniques: Sit, Walk, Heal

Meditation Exercises

Foreword

CFQ (Cosmic Freedom Qigong)

Chaoyi Fanhuan Qigong

Move from possession or from "with" to "without,"
From outstanding extraordinariness to Ordinariness.
To reveal a genuine harmonious qi flow that is refreshing, restful, and awakening.

CFQ Qigong is a path toward transformation to a state of comfort (at-ease-ness) and relaxation and being in a transparent consciousness (lightness). Practice CFQ letting-go to unload emotional and disease problems. This technique is considered a "method out of the world" compared with most approaches involving the "doing" or targeting of specific problems. CFQ healing emphasizes true relaxation and activating one's self-healing to do away with specific problems.

Practitioners can quickly move into a state of ego-less peace and transcendence (normally difficult to attain) with an expanded consciousness into their energy field. This serves as a basis for effective healing and advancement into deep insights.

CFQ exercising is an ageless breakthrough and comes from ancient Oriental energy medicine developed millennia ago. CFQ is a form of dynamic meditation. Qigong is not about absorbing and strengthen qi power or to absorb essence from air (a common misconception in some forms of Qigong). Nor is it about vigorous exercises based on the "sweat and burn" principle (equivalent to *burning away one's own life"*). No way is CFQ about using the power of the mind through concentration or visualization. True healing is *not* a mind function nor can it be created.

CFQ exercising uses principles that were traditionally regarded as "guarded secrets." It brings the mind (spirit) back to the body by switching from the *faculty of thinking to the faculty of feeling.*

The Energy-Spiritual Connection

The body is home to your spirit. Remember to come home from your mind to the body.

Mind-functions create tension knots and folds in one's energy field an cellular memories that stresses the body and disrupts physiological functions sowing the roots of disease problems, pains, and suffering. Every psychophysical crisis stems from a spiritual crisis.

Disease problems are eliminated through "detaching," "letting-go," or "undoing" and *not* by creating a healing effect through absorbing some "extraordinary qi-power" as is commonly proclaimed.

Master Yap SoonYeong
Penang, Malaysia

Preface

Over the past decade doing field trauma psychology and humanitarian work internationally, I have searched for a more universal approach to promoting healing, resilience and recovery in traumatized adults and children (in *Tao of Healing: The Incredible Golden Light*). While exploring my own roots in South East Asia, I met a remarkable Qigong healer and meditation teacher, Master Yap Soon Yeong of Penang Island. I have chronicled my journey based on the revelations of his ancient healing methods in meditation, Qigong, and TCM (Traditional Chinese Medicine) and how they have effectively helped numerous patients and students. This book is written to be a healing guide to practical resilience techniques.

Thus began my exposure to CFQ (Cosmic Freedom or *Chaoyi Fanhuan Qigong*), an energy and consciousness healing method that is proving effective in trauma cleansing, health promotion, and healing for otherwise insoluble health problems, and even for terminally ill patients. It proved beneficial to clear off trauma and PTSD effects in families affected by armed conflict in war zones such as Kosovo and Mindanao (Hiew, 2001) and sexually exploited children (Hiew, 2000). Since then I have presented workshops and seminars on CFQ as an innovative therapeutic tool for training health professionals in self-care and healing others. It is evident that CFQ training has produced hope and health benefits for those who have embraced it.

A new book co-authored with the CFQ Founder, Master Yap is, *Energy Medicine in CFQ Healing: Transforming the Body, Transcending Consciousness* (2002). This book is a contemporary medical breakthrough in the ancient field of

Qigong. To read this book is to understand how to realize one's capacity for an inherent gift of healing. Healing itself is simple, but genuine recovery requires more than treating the person as body parts or as mere physical matter.

Healing is about restoring consciousness (the resilient spirit) so that the body becomes relaxed, free from its energy burden. The mind's conflict is replaced by peace together with an energy flow that produces a harmonious consciousness.

This revised guidebook is entitled, *Dynamics of Qigong Healing* and has been expanded to serve as a training manual for the CFQ Level I Course in Meridian Healing (See Appendix for complete CFQ course description).

CFQ is a meridian based system (of energy channels in the body) as postulated in TCM and utilizes wisdom inherent in mind-body psychology or consciousness. Participants have observed therapeutic benefits within reasonably short periods of practicing CFQ. Essentially, practitioners learn how to neutralize and switch off stress responses, release energy blockages and unburden themselves of mental and emotional memories and reactions that traumatize mind and body.

For those who persevere in CFQ practice, homeostasis and equilibrium of energy flow are restored, eliminating disease symptoms and achieving complete healing. The purpose of this guidebook is to share with interested readers how they can activate their inner resilience to overcome life's problems and actualize their own full potential.

Chok C. Hiew, Ph.D.
Fredericton, New Brunswick

xiv

Acknowledgements

To our spiritual teachers and
to all who have experienced the Healing Light
Our gratitude and appreciation
Repeat the flowing joy!

Part One

Basics of
Traditional Healing Arts

Seven Facets of CFQ Healing

Radiant Energy dissolves the
Antecedents of disease and aging to cleanse
Dense noxious energies the culprit.
Inoculate against disease by letting go of
Antecedent disease energy carriers vaporized by
Nature's Golden Light pure
Transparence that illuminates all

From Tao of Healing:
The Incredible Golden Light (Hiew, 2000)

Introduction

Qigong for healing (Hiew & Yap, 2004, Figure 1) is an integral part of TCM or traditional Eastern Medicine (See also Wong, 1993; Ai et. al., 2001; Alladin; 2003). Interest in its incorporation into the health-care system has spread rapidly in North America (Final Report: White House Commission on Complementary and Alternative Medicine, 2002). There are currently five peer-reviewed journals (e.g., Journal of Alternative and Complementary Medicine) devoted to CAM (alternative medicine) that includes the medical applications of Qigong.

A Pub Med (National Library of Medicine) search on the health benefits of Qigong yields ever expanding evidence of its treatment efficacy (see also Sancier, 1996) that includes hypertension (Mayer, 1999); asthma (Reuther & Aldridge (1998); diabetes (Iwao et. al., 1999) immuno-competence (Lee et. al., 2001), and heroin addiction (Li, et. al., 2002).

The health benefits of Meridian Healing in CFQ Qigong training is evident from the numerous participants who reported such gains even within a couple of days of practice (Yap & Hiew, 2004). CFQ meridian exercises are simple and easy to learn yet can become a highly effective self-care tool to deal with psychological disabilities as well as physical problems. By opening out and flushing away the debased energy forces that congest and traumatize the head, torso and vital internal organs, resilience is activated and health restored.

Figure 1
A CFQ Resource Book

CFQ meridian exercises bring about a state of relaxation that impacts the energy-consciousness factor in the healing process. There is an expanded and regular energy flow in the body's meridians that, in turn, penetrates and shifts the brain to more relaxed and desirable states of consciousness. The overall outcome is a positive state of wellbeing and calmness. Some reported maladies that were effectively eliminated are highlighted below. For participants who trained from a few days to several weeks, health problems remedied include: Frozen shoulders and neck; chronic back, knee and ankle pains; fatigue and insomnia; infections, e.g., flu, urinary; gastrointestinal problems; anxiety/anger attacks and migraines.

With regular meridian exercising over a 6-12 month period (up to two years), chronic ailments that were eliminated include: Hypertension; Post-Traumatic Stress Disorders (PTSD); low blood pressure; speedy recovery of injuries/surgery; diabetes; depression; ovarian/uterine and prostate; obesity and age-related problems.

For those who cultivate CFQ meridian healing as the centerpiece of a transforming energy-consciousness lifestyle, their resilience is optimized to claim the human birthright to live long and healthy lives and hoped for spiritual insights (Hiew, 2000; Yap and Hiew, 2002). Clinical evidence reported enhanced coping with chronic diseases and even complete recovery for some. The practice is also a self-care tool that can deal with the ailments of normal living that traumatize mind and body.

This guidebook is useful as a training resource in meridian healing aimed at improving one's mental outlook, physical health and spiritual state. The objectives are:

1. Understand the insights of traditional Qigong and the principles of healing meridian movements. CFQ effectively flushes down the tension energy blockages in all the organs

and muscle systems stimulating smooth blood and harmonious pure qi (or ch'i) flow.

2. Apply these healing principles to learn a skillful means of holistically balancing energy flow in the meridian or energy channels. CFQ is a therapeutic tool for dealing with all psychological disturbances and illnesses and promotes health-protective resilience. The quantum healing equation is $e = mc^2$ (where e=energy flow; m= meridian body outlets and c^2 =cosmic consciousness or radiant Emptiness).

3. Understand the theory of a complete letting-go approach to health and advancement to a transcendent state of consciousness. This is the "original" wisdom-state of ultimate relaxation and peace that activates the innate self-repair response to rebound back to a state of harmony and optimal health.

References

Ai, A., Peterson, C., Gillespie B., Bolling, S., Jessup, et.al. (2001). Designing clinical trials on energy healing: Ancient art encounters medical science. *Alternative Therapy Health Med, 7(4),* 83-90.

Alladin, W. (2003). Meridian therapy in the 21st century: Interview with Chok Hiew. *Counseling Psychology Journal, 16(4),* 297-303.

Hiew, C. C. & Yap, S. Y. (2004*). True Qigong Healing Stories.* London: Paul Crompton, Inc.

Hiew, C. C. (2001). The course of healing toward peace. E. Abitol (Ed.*) Rites of Peace: Children and Armed Conflict.* Montreal: Peacemedia/Int. Bureau for Children's Rights.

Hiew, C. C. (2000). *Tao of Healing: The Incredible Golden Light Energy.* San Jose: Writer's Showcase, an imprint of iUniverse.com

Iwao, M., Kajiyama, S., Mori, H. & Ogaki, K. (1999). Effects of Qigong walking on diabetic patients: A pilot study. *Journal of Alternative Complement Med, 5(4)*, 353-8.

Li, W., Chen, K., & Mo, Z. (2002). Use of Qigong therapy in the detoxification of heroin addicts. *Alternative Therapy Health Med, 8(1)*, 50-4.

Litscher, G., Wenzel, G., Niederwieser, G., Schwarz, G. (2001). Effects of Qigong on brain function. *Neurological Research, 23(5)*, 501-5.

Knight M. (2002). Cosmic Freedom Qigong. *New Connexion: Journal of Conscious Evolution, 11(3)*, 1-3.

Lee Myeong-Soo, et. al.(2001). Psychoneuroimmunological effects of Qi-therapy: Preliminary study on the changes of level of anxiety, mood, cortisol, and melatonin and cellular function of neutrophil and NK cells. *Stress and Health, 1*, 17-24.

Mayer, M. (1999). Qigong and hypertension: A critique of research. *J Alternative Complement Med, 5(4)*, 371-82.

Reuther I. & Aldridge, D. (1998). Qigong Yangsheng as a complementary therapy in the management of asthma: A single-case appraisal. *J. Alternative Complement Med, 4(2)*, 173-83.

Sancier, K. (1996). Medical applications of Qigong. *Alternative Therapies, 2(1)*, 40-46.

Yap, S.Y. & Hiew, C. (2002). *Energy Medicine in CFQ Healing.* San Jose: Writers Club Press.

Wong, K. K. (1993*). Chi-kung for health and vitality: A practical approach to the art of energy.* Element Books.

Figure 2

Cosmic Freedom Qigong:

Chaoyi Fanhuan Qigong

They do not dwell in the past
Nor brood on the future
They abide in the present
Therefore they are radiant.

The Golden Sage

1

Health and Longevity:
The Resilience Factor*

Resilience is the capacity to move inward, let go of trauma, despair, problems and misfortunes and keep moving forward in life. Resilient people have a calm and relaxed outlook. Instead of brooding on past experiences and negative reactions they accept themselves and uphold a strong sense of responsibility and self-reliance. They tend to live by the positive human values of love, kindness, generosity, and a spirit of self-worth and commitment to others. (Figure 2).

Human societies' current success in lifespan extension and increased longevity need to be paralleled by an understanding of how to promote health across the lifespan. Much of the success of having attained longer life today is derived not from medical breakthroughs, but from instituting public health measures that raise standards of health and effectively prevent illness through sanitation, nutrition, clean water, food, and air as well as infant care. What has proven to be most health protective is adherence to healthier behavior and lifestyles. The present health care system, based entirely on medication and hospitals, needs to be augmented by individual self-care toward the goal of healthy aging.

---

*A version of this paper was published in the Japanese Health Psychology Journal (1998): Longevity and Healthy Aging, 6, 1-16.

Since psychological determinants are critical in the course of disease and health it is the application of psychosocial techniques of self-regulation that determines whether adults can rejuvenate and continue to remain healthy.

The biopsychosocial stress model conceptualizes the antecedents of disease (Engel, 1980) in terms of biological and psychosocial factors, while the public health approach leads to identifying host or person-environmental health protective factors that combine social-psychological as well as biological mechanisms (Winett, King, & Altman, 1988). In research on human resilience, i.e., how to stay healthy in unhealthy environments, health protective factors are identified as the presence of resilient inner strengths, competencies and external supports (Werner, 1992; Grotberg, 1999).

Of great importance is well-documented medical and stress research regarding the stress-illness relationship. The host-environment interaction creates the stress response. In one pathway, stressful events leading to unhealthy overt behaviors or, alternatively, to physiological reactions detrimental to health. Stress, indeed is the noxious agent and fundamental disease-causing antecedent that prevents well-being. As a result of the stress acquisition process, chronic stress reactions damage the body and produce illnesses (See Figure 3).

A "letting go response" based on the energy-consciousness perspective is proposed to remove harmful accumulated stress and tension for disease to be averted and health restored. Psychological science provides a diversity of mind and body techniques of stress reduction and relaxation. Contemporary Western techniques of stress and tension removal have their origins from the Eastern cultures (see Schultz, Lehrer, & Woolfolk, 1993) such as the practice of yoga and chi-kung (or Qigong from China).

Figure 3
Noxious Disease Agents and
Health Protective Factors:
A Biopsychosocial Model

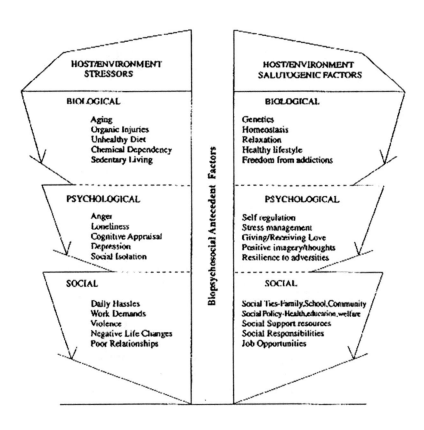

It is just as important to understand the person with a disease as it is to understand the disease in the person.

(Sir William Osler)

Qigong is the art of energy and mind cultivation through the letting go response. The practice is derived from ancient Taoist and Buddhist philosophies and has many adherents globally who practice it to promote health and longevity (Wong, 1993; Hiew, 1999).

In Eastern health practices, the accumulated antecedents are viewed as tension forces trapped in one's energy consciousness system that must be removed through the letting-go response to promote healthy aging (Hiew, 1997). A fundamental traditional Oriental medicine belief is that health is a function of the free flow of healthy vital bioenergy (chi or Qi) throughout the body's meridian or energy channel system. Illness symptoms are detected when the chi-energy circulation is blocked.

Oriental energy-therapies are widely available as alternative medicine in Western countries, using herbal remedies, acupuncture and massage to remove the blockages and restore the flow of energy. The assumption is that we have an inherent, sophisticated self-repair system that has the capacity to rejuvenate and maintain health and rid the body of any potential disease.

From the traditional Eastern energy medicine perspective, all biopsychosocial stimulants drawn inward and absorbed into the body have both tension and dynamic energy characteristics (Yap, 1995). The stress energy accumulates in layers of tension that eventually condenses into tension energy forces with a penetrative glue-like effect physically compressing, hardening, and distorting the body resulting in physiological imbalance and disease.

As tension forces build up, energy flow becomes lethargic, and consciousness becomes disturbed to harm healthy cellular growth and organ functions.

The glue-like tension force is similar to the residual, sticky waste products of cell metabolism (glycosylation) that has been proposed as the causal agent in biological aging (Austrad, 1997). Glycosylation products not only produce residual deposits that lead to diabetes, heart disease, and tumors but also accelerate cell death destroying healthy cells and growth.

The removal from the body of physical tension energy forces as well as bringing through the flow of relaxation energy is seen as anti-aging agents of health.

Based on the above review, the major proposition is the therapeutic value of the letting go response to remove stress and tension forces attached to the body (See Figure 4).

Three letting go strategies of resilience empowerment are proposed that collectively could optimize health, prevent illness, and promote healthy aging.

1. Identify the noxious agent causing the disease. The preventive strategy is to remove the biopsychosocial stress and disease-antecedents attached to the host (or person's energy system and consciousness).

2. Identify the transmission process whereby the noxious agents have invaded the host (person). The preventive strategy is to stop the transmission of disease energy-carriers.

3. Discover how to reduce vulnerability of the host to the noxious agents. The preventive strategy is to inoculate or strengthen the host's defenses by developing a truly relaxed state to neutralize or remove the disease agents.

Figure 4
Energy-Consciousness Model of De-Stressing

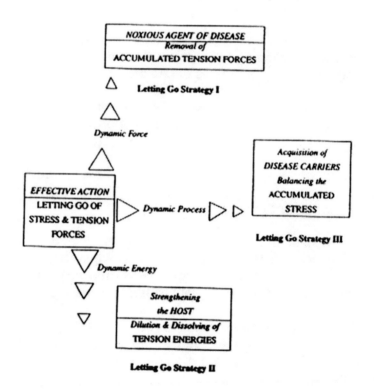

Nature is the healer of disease (Hippocrates: 460-377 BC)

The great error of our day of modern treatment of the human body is that physicians separate the soul from the body (Plato).

Letting Go of Psychosocial Stress

The "Person Effect" (Lynch, 1985) indicates the emotional and physical health influence of one human being on another and is the core of social support, which is the single, best non-physical predictor of cardiovascular health. The absence of the Person Effect, i.e., loneliness, is hazardous to health, the equivalent of an internal ticking time-bomb.

Social support and interaction is the key factor that reduces cardiovascular reactivity to acute psychological stress. It is difficult for a lonely human being who is totally socially isolated not to become ill. Without meaning in life, the will to continue living dissolves.

Affiliative ties or the capacity to love and show empathy as well as to receive love, is health protective. Social support comes from many diverse groups from family, friends, and local communities. In addition, in times of crisis, there is a need for social insulation in which social support is received from a few trusted individuals, confidants, intimates or a trained professional. Emotional inhibition, or holding back, of deeply rooted traumatizing feelings and unspoken negative emotions are safely expressed.

The letting go response, to express these emotions, frees the mind of stress-provoking thoughts and emotions and relaxes the body leading to improved health (Pennebaker, 1997).

At other times of recovery from acute or overwhelming stress, there is a need to be alone in social isolation for a period of self-reflection to seek relief. Such privacy, away from social pressures and demands, allows one to engage in a more relaxed mode of thinking, and clearer personal problem solving. Yet, personal privacy has to be balanced with the benefits of the Person Effect. The goal is to maintain emotional equilibrium by letting go of social stress.

For example, Ornish (1997) in the equivalent of a letting go program demonstrated that heart disease could be effectively reversed by integrating low fat dietary behavior, social support, group discussions, and self-reflection through meditation.

Strategy # 1: Removing the Noxious Agent

The social environment, which influences our thought and emotional processes, registers as noxious antecedents of disease. When negative thoughts and feelings from past adverse events are behaviorally inhibited, they have stressful consequences. Letting go of past stressful experiences trapped as tension forces in the body by overt expression of these negative emotions in a socially supportive context can prevent illnesses.

Letting Go of Unbalanced Living

There is a human tendency to acquire more and more of whatever object is consider being good or healthy to the point of excessive physical and mental over-stimulation. However, an omnipresent, inverted U-shaped relationship exists between the level or intensity of even healthy events and activities with negative outcomes. For example, blood cholesterol in large amount increase the risk of heart disease but is crucial for healthy functioning in small quantities. Medication that works well in treating heart disease is the same material (TNT) that in large quantities is used to make dynamite.

While exercise, vitamins, medicine, etc. are found to be good for the body, their benefits quickly peak in small or moderate quantities and an "overdose" is detrimental to health.

While acquisition of information is good for the brain, some people assumed more of the same to be even better, forgetting that it is quality (real knowledge), not quantity, that is more important. Here it is simply incorrect to uphold the "use it or lose it" notion. When the central nervous system is constantly 'overloaded' over the years, the by-product is brain abuse with negative effects such as dementia and Alzheimer's disease. The disease organ or body is almost always a victim of such unhelpful actions. Proponents of lifelong health have made a distinction between normal health in terms of absence of disease and optimal health that according to the World Health Organization, is a state of optimal functioning of body, mind, and spirit (Lieberman & Bruning, 1997).

Normal living leads to an acceptance of normal pathology or normal levels of dysfunction which do not achieve diagnosable levels much less achieve optimal health.

In Oriental medicine, the key is the diagnostic art of measuring pulses to detect hidden disease symptoms even before conventional Western medicine can do so. As people age, with ever increasing emotional, physical, and physiological imbalances, the early disease symptoms then become diagnosable by Western medicine. The accumulated tensions and excesses of a lifetime make the host vulnerable and poor health becomes evident.

Through the cultivation of the letting go response, there is less accumulation of chronic stress and tension forces, and consequently less damage to the body. For example, Tapanya and Hiew (See Hiew, 1998) reported recruiting diabetic patients for a hospital in Northern Thailand in a six-week intervention program involving social support, relaxation training and breathing meditation. Participants not only expressed reduction in their perceived stress, but also reduced and stabilized their blood sugar levels.

Letting go of the acquisition tendency to achieve a more relaxed pace of living maintains health by drawing in less tension or disease carriers.

Strategy # 2: Stopping the Transmission of Disease Carriers

Positive thoughts can produce positive emotions and behaviors that have health protective consequences but when unbalanced are also stressful. This follows the "more is less" rule of stressful living. Letting go of the acquisition tendency prevents the transmission of disease-carriers and reduces the resultant excessive stress accumulation. The body is restored back to internal balance to a more optimal relaxed state to halt disease development and its progression.

Letting Go of the Ego Self

Mind-body communication ensures that the quality of our thoughts and emotions impacts on the body's health, as proposed in the previous two strategies of letting go. What is critical to health is a relaxed mind, free from stress-provoking thoughts and emotions, so that the body's internal balance is sustained. On another dimension, our thoughts and emotions come from our consciousness, a more holistic concept of who we are, in terms of chi-energy. A stressed consciousness needs to be replaced with peace.

According to ancient eastern philosophy that is verified by modern quantum physics, all matter is energy and all things are connected. Taoism holds that the origin of the universe is pure or vibrant cosmic energy, which is positively and negatively charged, creating constant change. This creative change gives rise to the universe of physical reality and all its myriad inanimate and living forms.

In brief, it is this universal pure chi-energy that breathes life in humans and every living plant and animal.

Research indicates that people who response to biopsychosocial stressful events and conditions with potent negative emotions acquire a disease-prone personality and are more susceptible to chronic diseases. The Type A personality (hot-tempered and driven) is prone to cardiovascular disease (Spielberger, et. al., 1995) while the Type C (emotionally inhibited and over-cooperative) is vulnerable to cancer (Eysenck, 1994).

The good news is that for those who are able to transform their hearts, minds, and behaviors, disease is reversed and they regain their health. Changing their lives in this way have led to becoming healthier personalities who are characterized by cheerful optimism, high self-esteem, positive relationships, physiological relaxation (Holahan & Moos, 1985) and a commitment in the pursuit of transcendent values and goals (Maslow, 1968; Friedman & Ulmer, 1984).

Recent research (Atwater, 1997) revealed that the benefits of effective meditation techniques comes with initially dissociating from ordinary states of consciousness and ego-involvement and shifting to an EEG-measurable transcending consciousness characterized by tranquil affect states, peace and a concern for others. A commitment to transcendent goals and values beyond oneself such as helping others or altruistic or prosocial behavior, is the hallmark of meditators cultivating the letting go response (Alexander, Rainforth, & Gelderloos, 1991). Such harmonious behavior balances the individual internally together with the surrounding environment. Greater health accrues to the individual who radiates transcendent energies to others.

All Eastern meditative practices are aimed at ultimately letting go of an attachment to a separate personal identity. Here the letting go is to detach from the dense energies and disown the realities of the ego-self and its flawed physical body. The ideal is to expand consciousness beyond one's physical boundaries to embrace and become one with the pure or cosmic energy, the ultimate relaxed state. We trade in our tired, residual energy and tension forces that cling to our ego-self and personal identity in exchange for the more vibrant boundless energy of our cosmic self freely available to all living things (Figure 5).

The self-repair or healing response becomes readily activated to maintain health and regeneration throughout the life span of the transformed individual.

Strategy # 3: Restoring the Self-Repair Response

Thoughts of purity, free from stressful egocentric needs (for example, altruistic states of being such as loving-kindness and joyous peace), are non-attaching in nature and can be brought into consciousness as relaxation energy. This is the ultimate letting go process to be free from the life-long acquisition and creation of personal identity. Letting go of the dense disease-causing tension forces and condensed stress-energy is possible by detaching from one's personality and the mind-body limitations through expanding one's consciousness. The energy of transcendent thought or higher consciousness shifts and releases an optimal self-repair response.

Opening to this purer energy detaches the body from impurities by diluting, dissolving, and ejecting the dense tension forces clinging to the body and responsible for disease and aging.

Figure 5
Letting Go Principle of Tao

The Art of Wu Wei

The Way of the Heart (xin-fa):

*Action in non-action: To Undo by Non-doing
with Non-Intention*

Healing the Past: Pain & Trauma

Every psychological and pathological problem has an emotional component. When a person is a victim of a sudden or prolonged traumatic experience or stressful event, mishap, violence, injustice or loss, a permanent emotional impact is formed. S/he can become disoriented as the emotional pain and suffering lingers. Natural responses, then, are dictated by energy forces and memories of the incident. The victim is dragged down with haunting memories or compulsive negative thoughts.

By dwelling in and following the negative thoughts and emotions, further pain, hatred, anger, and fear are in turn aggravated thus trapping the victim in an undesirable or altered psychological state. By attempting to reconcile and suppress the incident the victim, in this case, becomes further entangled in emotions and feels powerless against the compulsive undesirable thoughts.

Energy & States of Consciousness

Trauma energy of the painful past can give rise to excessive and uncontrollable responses that are quite strong and easily activated. When triggered, energy forces within the five senses become aroused and cause muscular tension. This biases perception and spreads out into a field that extends into the subconscious.

The altered state or information field manifests energetically as a dark cloud, and such clouds can function like a shield. When this occurs, the victim becomes dominated and controlled by this field and ceases to have normally flexible and adaptive thinking functions and indeed the person's actions are increasingly dictated by this field. If one sees images or hears voices within the reality in this energy field, hallucinations manifest.

In drug-induced states, the drug affects a surge of energy, shielding off normal consciousness. If the person is addicted, then his or her usual consciousness and control can actually be obstructed by the energy shield.

Such an energy field usually dissipates its forces in time. But it wreaks havoc before partially wearing out. The remaining dysfunctional energy tends to be reabsorbed into the energy field. After the energy field settles back into appropriate levels of consciousness, the person functions normally again. But with each outbreak, energy forces become stronger and the next outbreak can occur more easily and with greater power.

Outbursts can occur in response to extreme emotional arousal causing such feelings as excessive anger, fear, or despair. Once such an outburst occurs, it needs to be dealt with properly, or it can become a habit within the person's consciousness that can be readily triggered in the next attack.

Even normal healthy people can switch into an altered state of rage if sufficiently aroused. In such cases, the person feels agonized by the gripping effect of the energy force field. At this point, s/he is in an altered state and their normal flexible mind is shielded off. Energy field forces, seeking to relief the agony dictate actions.

If one becomes deeply involved, there can be a loss of responsibility and morality. A better alternative is to learn to accept oneself as we are.

Accept the fact that the incident has happened and is now in the past, regardless of what may have gone on or what damage may have been inflicted. The wiser path is to pick oneself up and move ahead, to claim one's rightful entitlement to health. By moving forward without blame, the negative thoughts have no chance to catch up.

Resilient people are wonderfully able when it comes to getting over a trauma, misfortune or despair. They have an optimistic and cheerful outlook, and are more relaxed. They tend to live by the positive human values of love, kindness, generosity, responsibility, self-worth, and spiritual faith. An ability to accept oneself and uphold a strong sense of responsibility and commitment to others make a person resilient.

Undesirable forces that undermine resilience include self-centeredness, pride, worrisome thinking, and perfectionism, having unrealistic expectations, lacking in emotional expression, hostility, and over-reacting to problems.

Science no longer upholds the notion that all memory resides in the brain. We now know that the organs and muscles also contain some of our memories. This can explain the effects of emotional trauma. The assumption of memory storage solely in the brain implies that all memories could be altered or erased. This belief counters experience. The more one attempts to control or forget memories, the stronger they bounce back. In times of mental distress, this no-win "remedy" aggravates the situation.

Further, it is an ineffective strategy to encourage a psychologically or physically fatigued person to rest to get over their problems. By resting, the person is spending more time fabricating fatigue.

Normal rest or inactivity is really no rest, but is rather more time for a counterproductive dwelling on one's problems. The same holds for depression, anxiety and unhappy emotional states. The best way is to move ahead and carry on with life; being meaningfully busy so that negative thoughts cannot catch up.

Acceptance & Moving On

Dealing with people with psychological disorders may be extremely complex and requires a good deal of tolerance. Their attitude and mind-set may make it difficult to please them; their mood swings can render their behavior unpredictable; they may be over-sensitive and over-react to petty or unrelated issues. As their social contacts dwindle and they become isolated, relatives and loved ones who are close to them not only suffer with them but also become a convenient outlet on which they vent their frustrations. The family and caregivers may suffer even more than the patients. Psychological problems are unique because the mind is capable of repeating a compulsive thought with such intensity that normal work and activity can be greatly disturbed.

Generally, people have little idea how the mind operates. It does not stop for even a second. When a person is thinking, the mind absorbs and is absorbed by the subject matter, whereas when one is involved in physical activity, the mind functions along with the activity. When resting, without any particular thought (idling), the mind wanders and becomes trapped in thoughts with strong emotional attachments.

When a person sleeps, the mind becomes dissociated from both the body's senses and the external environment, leaving the mind to carry on its own sorting, processing, and assimilating of energy memories.

Thus, at no time does the mind stop. Neither can thoughts stop. They revolve around some object of incessant thinking. If the person is focused on something of great interest, he or she is able to sidetrack other interfering thoughts. Otherwise, if allowed to function on its own, every memory fights to be heard. The ones that speak most strongly are those with deep emotional involvement or events with great physical impact.

Traumatic episodes are, of course, the ones that tend to cause deep emotional involvement. Similarly, objects of preferential mental activity have deep emotional roots and any attempt to fight or control such thoughts only fabricates stronger thoughts.

To minimize being controlled by the gripping and suffocating effects of psychological problems requires moving ahead with normal life and activities. This reduces the available time within which the mind is allowed to revictimize the victim. Whatever the problem, real or imagined, the victim must be brave enough to leave it behind.

The past cannot be lived again differently. Once one has learned the truth of the past event, there is absolutely no need to recall it, or to think about its right or wrong, good or bad qualities.

Do not allow the problem to drag the victim down to become deprived of the rights, privileges, and entitlement to a happy future. Willingness to change attitude is crucial if the person is to leave the psychological problem behind and proceed with normal life. It is also crucial to help a former victim return to a normal state of consciousness.

However, more often than not, the psychologically disabled continues to suffer low efficiency in work, and a lack interest and initiative. This is understandable. Normal work and activities are mundane compared to the thrills and chills of mental adventures or fantasies and even of being fearful. To overcome this, they need to develop a strong sense of responsibility, backed by positive values. To completely eliminate the disturbing thoughts that exist as energy memories, embarking on the energy-healing practice is a truly positive action (See Figure 6).

Figure 6
Tao of Healing

Tune in: To CFQ meridian motion-and-emotion cleansing

Turn on: Your resilient smile

Drop out: Noxious energy burdening body and mind

Undo: Antecedent cause of confusion, pain, and illness

Freedom's just another word
For nothing left to lose
                    Me & Bobby McGee

References

Alexander, C. N., Rainforth, M. V., & Gelderloos, P. (1991). Transcendental meditation, self-actualization, and psychological health: A conceptual overview and statistical meta-analysis. *Journal of Social Behavior and Personality, 6, 189-247.*

Atwater, H. (1997). Accessing anomalous states of consciousness with a binaural beat technology. *Journal of Scientific Exploration, 11(3),* 263-274.

Austrad, S.N. (1997). *Why we age.* New York: John Wiley.

Engel, G. L. (1980). The clinical application of the biopsychosocial model. *Amer. J. of Psychiatry, 137,* 535-544.

Eysenck, H. J. (1994). Cancer, personality, and stress: Prediction and prevention. *Advances in Behavioral Research and Therapy, 16,* 167-215.

Friedman, M. & Ulmer, D. (1984). *Treating Type A behavior.* NY: Random House.

Grotberg, E, (1999). Tapping your inner strengths: How to find the resilience to deal with anything. Oakland: New Harbinger Publications.

Hiew, C. C. (1998). *Longevity and healthy aging: The self-repair response.* Japanese Health Psychology, *6,* 1-16.

Hiew, C. C. (1997). Cultivating the gold-body energy. Presented at *the International Study of Subtle Energies and Energy Medicine.* Boulder, Colorado

Hiew, C. & Yap, SY. (1999). CFQ energy therapy. In *Annual Conference of Energy Psychology,* Toronto, Canada.

Lieberman, S., & Bruning, N. (1997). *The real vitamin and mineral book.* NY: Avery Books.

Lynch J. J. (1985). *The language of the heart.* New York: Basic Books.

Maslow, A. H. (1968). *Toward a psychology of being.* New York: Van Nostrand Reinhold.

Ornish, D. (1997*). Love and survival: The scientific basis for the healing power of intimacy.* NY: Harper.

Pennebaker, J.W. (1997). *Opening up: The healing power of expressing emotions.* NY: Guilford.

Schultz, J. H., Lehrer, P. M., & Woolfolk, R. L. (Eds.) (1993). *Principles and practice of stress management* N Y: Guilford

Spielberger, C. D., Ritterband, L. M., Sydeman, S. J., Reheiser, E.C., & Unger, K. (1995). Assessment of emotional states and personality traits: Measuring psychological vital signs. In *J. N. Butcher (Ed.) Clinical personality assessment: Practical approaches.* New York: Oxford University Press.

Werner, E. E.(1992). The children of Kauai: Resilience and recovery in adolescence and adulthood. *Journal of Adolescent Health, 13*, 262-268.

Winett, R. A, King, A.C., & Altman, D.G. (1988). *Health psychology and public health: An integrative approach.* NY: Pergamon.

Wong, K. K. (1993). *Chi-kung for health and vitality: A practical approach to the art of energy.* Element Books.

Yap, S.Y. (1995). Alternative medicine: Energy healing. Presented at *the Professional Conference of the Monroe Institute.* Virginia: Faber.

Figure 7
Meridian e-Motion (Energy Movements)

Cleanse the meridians and harness bioenergy
Harmonize whole-body meridian energy flow
Undo the tension trapped that cause problems
Replace a conflict-consciousness with relaxation
Clear a path to connect with our greatest healer:
Peace!

2

A Bio-Energy Healing Model

TCM (Traditional Chinese Medicine) is an ancient healing system from *the Huangti Nei Ching* or the Yellow Emperor's Classic on Internal Medicine, a 24-volume medical text that was written around 2500 B. C. It is an energy medicine that focuses on regulation of a healthy bioenergy flow in the body's meridians (positive and negative) and energy system through physical techniques such as acupuncture, massage and herbs. TCM also assumes the necessity for *"medicine for the heart"* in healing emotional disturbances but leaves this to other disciplines such as Taoism, Buddhism and Qigong.

This guidebook introduces CFQ, a meridian-based therapy rooted in meditation and Taoist principles of living in peace and health. CFQ's core philosophy is the *Heart Sutra* of Perfect Understanding on the nature of existence. CFQ's dynamic exercises establish a complete letting-go healing process that eliminates the fundamental cause of all emotional, mental, and physical disabilities (debased noxious energy trapped within) and provides a true cure of all potential diseases in living (See Figure 7).

CFQ Background

Cosmic Freedom or Chaoyi Fanhuan Qi (CFQ) is a Qigong meridian-based approach (Hiew & Yap, 1999) involving whole-body energy exercise and healing consciousness effective in treating psychological burdens and bioenergy imbalance diseases.

CFQ reveals the guarded secrets of ancient cosmic ch'i or qi healing essential to train in this natural, ultimate relaxation energy technique. Cosmic qi energy is accessed to root out the trapped tension energy forces, the fundamental cause of emotional trauma, disease and aging hiding in body, mind and spirit.

CFQ meridian healing removes the tension burden in the body, stops anxiety in the mind, and stills the heart to reduce emotional disturbances and conflicts. The practitioner transmits radiant qi by means of CFQ motion to effectively loosen the dense energy forces, sinking, and clearing out the bioenergy blockages. Energy flow becomes smooth and balanced eliminating trapped biopsychosocial trauma and conflicts.

Trauma and negative emotions are reversed and "undone" by putting the body's meridians in motion coupled with a liberating luminous consciousness to activate the wisdom of the body toward resilience and full recovery. CFQ dynamic exercises establish a complete healing process that eliminates the fundamental cause of all emotional, mental, and physical disabilities and provides a true cure of all potential diseases in living.

The word qi is today taken to mean bioenergy in the body's system. However, in ancient times people used Qigong to harmonize themselves to better deal with life situations. It appears to be a practical way or system to pacify emotions and thoughts to enhance their resilience to face adversities wisely.

In this context, CFQ meridian healing is defined as a energy system of practical methods of dealing with consciousness in order to enhance resilience and energy flow to activate the inherent self-repair response and optimize health *(Energy Medicine in CFQ Healing by Yap & Hiew, 2002).*

Fundamental Principles of Qigong

I. Relaxation. The word for relaxation is clearly understood as meaning to "let loose," or to let go and loosen oneself. It literally means to do away with, or undoing something that has been created or dropping off one's strength. Conventional exercise and relaxation techniques taught are not truly relaxing. The mistake lies in the conception of relaxation: it should be about doing away with what is not relaxed rather than creating a relaxation effect!

II. Stillness. Stillness should occur at the mental level and beyond, i.e., within the consciousness itself. When the body is truly relaxed, the person has a peaceful consciousness. He or she feels peaceful and with this peace will not be overly disturbed by the mind or outside stimulation. Only if the consciousness is still can the body settle down into Stillness. The character for "peace" means harmonized qi. Remember this: *Peace is the greatest healer!*

III. Naturalness. The core of ancient teaching is that humans are part of nature. First, there must be a basic understanding of the laws of Nature to harmonize oneself so that you can live well with Nature. To be natural therefore means that you should not be creating disharmony that conflicts with Nature as in greedily absorbing her energy. It simply means to relax, be open or be at ease. And find peace.

IV. Regulation of the Body, Breathing, and Heart. In the self-regulation of cognitions, emotions and behaviors, the above three principles are put into practice. But over-emphasis on any single aspect can be dangerously misleading.

Emphasizing the body suggests that one should make oneself strong, but strength contradicts physical looseness for smooth energy flow. An emphasis on breathing suggests that one must absorb the nourishment or "essence"from the air but those conflicts with Nature rather than harmonizing. Emphasis on the heart would not lead to peace but to an inclination to overwork the mind with thinking and visualizing.

V. Breathing, Essence from Air, and Visualization. The common misconception, among most practitioners and Qigong masters, seems to be that qi is necessary for proper physical functioning. This misinterpretation gives rise to the dangerous misdirection that it ought to be enhanced, strengthened, and increased in order to optimize health.

The common speculation is that this essence comes from the air. So you are advised how to breathe and how to process the essence from air through mental activity. This is untrue and will not produce healing results.

Bioenergy in the body is unquantifiable. The idea of strengthening, enhancing or increasing the volume of qi is mere wishful speculation and brings much harm by creating panic for fear of *"losing qi."*

Chinese medicine teaches about enhancing bioenergy flow but not about increasing the volume of bioenergy. The pursuit of peace and harmony to bring about good health and resilience is the primary objective.

VI. Concept of Energy Channels (Meridians). In TCM, the body is served by a network-like system of channels or meridians for the flow of bioenergy (qi). There are altogether 12 major bilateral meridians and eight special meridians.

CFQ practices the wide-open method that does not require (nor desirable) to apply detailed knowledge about the meridians and the acupoints (more than 360 of them).

Being over-concerned with such knowledge limits the use of radiant energy and restricts its healing effect.

The 12 major meridians are therefore summarized and simplified for the purpose of the CFQ meridian exercises. The hand's three yin meridians are straight lines that run downward along the inner arms to the fingers. The foot's three yin meridians are straight lines that run upward along the inner legs from the feet. All the six yin meridians are found in front of the torso.

The hand's three yang meridians are straight lines that run upward along the outer arms from the fingers. The foot's three yang meridians are straight lines that run downward along the outer legs to the feet; and all the six yang meridians are found at the back of the torso gathering at the head.

Of the eight special meridians, three of them are selected (belt, front and back torso) to be harnessed in the CFQ exercises. They are:

1. The *jen* meridian that runs along the center line of the front of the torso,
2. The *tu* meridian that runs upward along the center line of the back of the torso to the head.
3. The belt meridian that runs round the waist below the navel.

By working on these meridians the whole body's systems will be cleansed and regulated. Qi-flow enhances blood flow. More flow of the qi along the 12 major meridians enhances optimum function of all the internal organs which, in turn, ensures that the faculties of the six senses are properly regulated and repaired. Bioenergy or qi flowing through the meridians is fluid-like and responds to electrical stimulation.

For harmonious function of the body systems the meridians must be cleared of blockages and the yin and yang must be balanced. Such a state is not easily attainable by physical interference of say TCM, acupuncture, or herbs. It is also easily disrupted by changes in moods and emotional states. However, the radiant energy generated by CFQ meridian exercises to produce a peaceful, non-fabricating letting go mind-set can readily clear any blockages and ensures that the yin and yang are properly balanced (See Figure 8).

VII. The Mind in TCM. The *'Nei Ching'*, the most ancient substantive Oriental medical book, states, *"If a person is peaceful, calm and not greedy, his real energy is harmonious. If he guards his spirit against outside disturbances, diseases find no way to attack him."*

Oriental Medicine advocates that the internal emotional or consciousness factor is the primary cause of disease while external influences are secondary. However, it chose the easy way out by stating that diseases of the heart (or mind/consciousness) must be cured by the *"medicine of the heart."* Medicine of the heart means to calm and harmonize one's thoughts.

Accepting that the indigenous medical profession was historically limited in status and prestige, such teachings were developed outside of TCM. Oriental medicine confined its work on physical therapies focused on the body.

Optimum health is crucially dependent on the ability to deal with one's emotions and thoughts, which again depends on a positive state of consciousness flowing with peace, calmness, harmony, and tranquility.

These healing characteristics are of course today affirmed by psychological and medical science. In order for such suggestions to be effective, one must cultivate skillful methods to actively change the energy-consciousness factor.

Figure 8
Healing: Releasing debased energy

(Hollow yin-movements)

(Solid yang-movements)

Fundamentally, the method generates a smooth flow of bioenergy in the body in order that the positive qualities be inculcated into a person's state of consciousness. However, this does not imply increasing and strengthening the energy which is not beneficial to the body. The tendency to do so gives rise to absorbing-fabricating-creating-grasping tendencies in a person, a process that disrupts harmony and, in turn, causes turbulence to disturb peace at the expense of health.

CFQ adheres completely to the three fundamental principles of relaxation, stillness, and naturalness. While conventional Qigong methods proclaim adherence to these principles, their practices often contradict them as they emphasize acquisition, creating/visualization tendencies.

3

Secrets of Traditional Healing

In ancient times, it was a tradition for masters of martial or esoteric healing arts to deliberately withhold essential principles or vital insights. Such a practice meant that, today, teachers and practitioners are unaware of the important features, unsure of how to cultivate, and unable to heal (Figure 9).

Without the knowledge of these "guarded secrets," any Qigong practice is, at best, mediocre in effectiveness. These secrets are described in detail for you here in order to help its promotion. They are in fact fully incorporated in the CFQ techniques taught.

1. Downward Flushing. *When the bioenergy sinks down, hundreds of diseases disappear.* TCM claims that the one method that cures all diseases is to drain down the bioenergy. But can it be done? Without thorough knowledge about how to bring the energy down and out, the above saying remains a concept.

Where the mind reaches, bioenergy reaches. Most Qigong techniques use visualization to harness qi flow and bring down the qi. However, proper visualization techniques are not easy to master. Insufficient concentration renders the technique ineffective. Over-concentration may lead to qi congestion with serious health consequences.

Figure 9
Lao Tzu riding off into the Sunset

Going beyond the ordinary
Shedding the orthodox
In radiant Emptiness
Return to the Origin and Truth
The Self-nature reveals.

(Hiew, 2000). Tao of Healing: The Incredible Golden Light.

Even if visualization is correctly practiced, the effect may not be long-term as it results from the mind's creation whereas the cause of blockages and suspension is tension, which can only be reduced by the letting-go process. Visualization at best creates a letting-go intention on top of the normal creation process of the mind and does not lead to real letting-go. This process will excite the mind to the extent that unknowingly the desire-mind takes over and switches to an absorption/creation process.

No visualization is required at all in CFQ exercises. What is required is to do each movement directly. The simplicity of the steps ensures that stale tension energy has no room to hide in the body but flows downward and outward through the limbs. Once reaching the extremities (hands and feet), it can no longer adhere on the body but is freed into the cosmos. The body naturally exchanges with and replaces stale tension energy with pure cosmic energy.

II. Speed. Perform the exercises slowly and easily. The speed of bioenergy flow is almost the same as breathing. Fast movements do not encourage energy flow but instead hinder its flow. On the other hand, if the movements are too slow, energy flow will be constrained.

III. Breathing. Breathe naturally throughout the exercises (except as instructed in the "preparation" and "conclusion" procedures. Attempts to blend breathing with movements (as in other Qigong methods), may cause chest congestion and heart ailments. You do one thing at a time (only concerned with movements, not breathing). This is the secret to harmony.

CFQ practice is neither about learning how to breathe nor absorbing the essence from air. While relaxation and improvement to health are apparent using breathing techniques, the way a person breathes and the depth of one's breathing are dependent on the person's physiological condition.   Therefore, to change one's style by artificially introducing a method of breathing may bring undesirable consequences.

IV. Loose Hollow Movements. Performing the exercises without using the slightest strain or strength ensures that energy and blood flow smoothly.   Strength and physical exertion obstructs bioenergy flow and gives rise to a tensing effect that hinders physiological functions.

With the non-use of strength, the trapped tension melts away.   The organization of cells and the space between them also become extended thus facilitating proper physiological functions, waste removal, cell repair, and replacement. Loose or effortless movements are equivalent to the "hollow" or yin concept. This alone is unable to go in deep enough to clear internal energy blockages.

To do so, "solid" inner strength movements *(nei jing)* is used to push out any stale residual tension by alternating between the hollow movements. It is not easy to ensure the looseness of movements. Beginners will be using plenty of strength without realizing it. Their bodies are also stiff and inflexible.

With prolonged practice, gradually understand and appreciate the nature of such movements. Continue to practice, doing it right by reducing strength and loosening further.

IV. Relaxing the Hamstring (*song kua*). The words 'song kua' is commonly used in martial arts involving soft movements and Qigong. But practitioners seldom seem to have done this movement correctly. *"Ku"* is the region where the hamstring meets the groin at the hip.

The most conducive stance for the proper execution of *'song kua'* is when both feet are one foot apart and parallel to each other. From the normal relaxed standing position, loosen and bend the knees in order to drop your body weight. If properly done, you should feel:

1.   A loosening all over your body including the shoulder and chest as if some binding force is removed;
2.   The contact between your feet and the ground becomes firmer and your body weight feels like being transferred to under your feet; and
3.   A comforting, highly pleasant sensation in the groin

The following guide will ensure that you do that *(song kua)* correctly:

1. The angle of the knee bent should be about 30 degrees. Bending beyond 30 degrees will render the loosening ineffective. For those with knee pains or other restrictive problems, just loosen with a slight drop (increase gradually when conditions improve).
2. Make sure that you drop your strength completely. In particular, your neck, shoulders, lower back, thighs, calves and toes should be void of strength.
3. If you look down, the toes should be visible. That means the kneecaps should not protrude beyond the toes. Drop the buttocks as if it is on a high chair.
4. Make sure that you are not pushing your hip to the back. Most beginners are so stiff that when they perform the *'song kua'* they tend to push their hip forward and lean backward. This is an extremely bad posture that will not result in any relaxing effect at all. This simple procedure requires a long period of practice to perfect.

When properly done, this movement causes an instantaneous improvement for people with hypertension. It can also provide rapid relief from most chronic pains and for common infections such as colds and flu. It is most effective when combined with "*fa jing*" to release stale inner strength (see below for the dynamic duo: *song kua fa jing* motion). Perform them in a dynamic manner rather than holding each step in a stationary manner.

VI. Releasing the Stale Inner Strength *(fa jing)*.

Exertion of any kind during each exercise results in trapped inner strength. Slowly begin the movement with looseness. Allow the palms to arch upward and hold them unmoving for a short while (2 to 5 seconds). This is done together with 'song kua' with slightly bent knees. In the correct procedure, you should feel a kind of rigidity spread evenly throughout your palms and fingers. This "finger stretching" is matched similarly to the firmness you feel under your feet with the 'song kua' position.

Care is taken not to over-emphasize the hands during *fa jing* as the proper sinking of *"song kua"* is equally important for the bioenergy to flow downward and outward. Also, ensure that strength is not left in any part of the body including the joints. Consequently, internal parts such as the tendons and muscles hidden under the surface muscles are extended and elongate to achieve maximum physical opening effect.

It optimizes energy and blood flow, thus enhancing the replacement of disharmony with the energy of peace required for holistic wellbeing. With the *'song kua fa jing'* dynamic movement (Figure 10), energy flow along all the six yin-meridians of the hands and feet are enhanced.

The stale inner-strength is projected outward to exchange with the pure cosmic energy that flows back along the six yang-meridians when performing the effortless movements.

VII. The Method of the Heart *(xin fa).* In the past, *"xin fa"* was only taught to ordained disciples and with the knowledge *of xin fa* the progress of a novice becomes much faster. Today, *xin fa* is absent in most disciplines of meditation, Qigong, and martial arts. The principle here is to have an attitude of calmness.

One cannot truly calm down by controlling the mind, as it will rebel against the pressure you introduce. You end up even more restless. Neither can the person be successful trying to calm down the body as one ends up using a lot of strength and exerting will power to hold still. That strengthens your ego and increases your energy load.

Figure 10
Healing: Doing the fa jing (Movement 1)

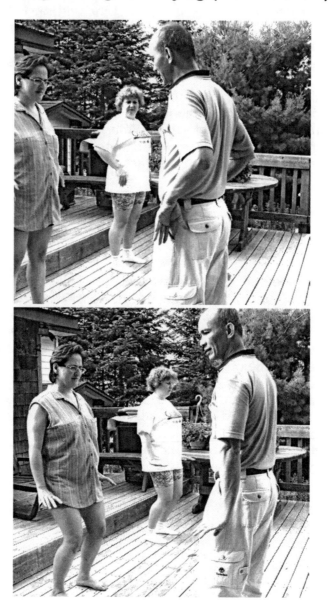

The purpose of CFQ methods and exercises is to cultivate peace. First, we must calm the heart, called *"the Unmoved Heart."* The Unmoved Heart only comes about when it is not attached to any condition: no intention, no pressure, and no differences between right and wrong, successes or failures. You are not even bothered about your problems (illness or pains included), not to speak of wanting to recover from it.

As for the mind, it can continue to function and think even when doing the exercises. Just let it be. Do not even attempt to control it as that gives rise to a fight that you can never win. Just go ahead with your exercise in a restful and relaxing manner.

The thoughts activated by the practice do not affect you so long as you ignore them. These thoughts might encourage a "self-sabotage" to stop practicing.

As you dissolve and dilute the debased energy blockages, the energy burden you carry will vanish!

This Stillness is the greatest secret of healing--that you are not bothered by anything. No more "I want..." this or that for the mind to do or body to tense up. You do not even want to heal yourself!

True cures come from non-doing, as the wisdom of your body knows best. Doing something no doubt can be a remedy but may not bring about a true cure.

Only the peace revealed in one's consciousness can activate the resilience to rebound back to health.

Figure 11
Biopsychosocial Trauma & the Energy Absorption Reflex

Universal Energy Flow

Energy Absorption Reflex

Mind/Brain		Body
	⇓	
1. Psychosocial Trauma	Debased energy conversion	Biological Trauma
	⇓	
2. Tension Energy Dark Cloud	Bioenergy Blockages	Energy Suspension

⇓

Muscle Tension/Hardening
Body Misalignment
Blood Flow Restriction
Organs Dysfunctional
Cells Sicken & Decline

⇓

Distress-Depression-Disorder-Disease

4

Energy Imbalances & Illnesses

Meridian bioenergy flow is the basis of TCM (Traditional Chinese Medicine). It says that if qi (bioenergy) and blood flow smoothly, the body's immunity to hundreds of diseases is strengthened. Poor energy flow gives rise to diseases and diseases further hinder bioenergy flow. Problems in life (psychosocial disturbances as well as diseases) arise from loading one's body and consciousness at the energy level, which becomes a burden that affects the physical, mental and spiritual components.

In Buddhist and Taoist meditative traditions, body, brain, and spiritual consciousness are mutually influencing. Purification must cleanse energy forces from the entire consciousness. The trapped energy burden creates blockages that give rise to imbalances in mind and mental functioning such as lethargy, weaknesses, depression, and psychological disturbances that hamper all vital physiological functions. This is the mind-body energy connection (See Figure 11).

To restore health is simply to restore bioenergy flow and clear away blockages (using the Hexagram Dance). To do so move the body parts to unwind and release the tension-blockages, even for those who have become weakened by disease. This awakens the inner resilience by replacing conflicts with a calm, relaxed state of consciousness instead of allowing the weakening process (from a confused helpless mind) to dominate (Figure 12).

Figure 12
Way of the Heart

Undoing with the Hexagram

The Heart knows what reason cannot
Peace opens.

Nothing needs to be added to reverse the disease process as healing is initiated when the body's self-repair response is activated. The body's organs function optimally so that regeneration and healing results. Indeed, reversing the disease process is working against the odds. When a person is not doing anything or taking action to help oneself, the mind has all the time in the world for self-sabotage that fabricates a strengthening of the disease process.

The practice of CFQ is recommended as a positive tool to dissolve any pathological behavior, trait, emotion, or compulsive thought through the letting-go approach. This approach removes the problems from deep within the spiritual realm and out through the mental-emotional and the physical body levels. It enables shifting from a pathological state of consciousness to a normal state. It anchors this achievement of balance in a beneficial state of consciousness.

Meridian Exercises: The Hexagram Dance facilitates a whole-body unloading of the problem from within to liberate one's own essential deep peace. The Butterfly Shake & Lotus Walk is practiced to complement the CFQ meridian exercises. An average person might be able to practice the 7-movements for about one hour, which might involve three or four sets. This hour program might be repeated two or three times a day for those with psychological problems. More repetitions of the meridian exercises can be beneficial. When encountering compulsive thoughts, avoid them by butterfly shaking or lotus walking (say, half hour for each) until such emotional spells dissipate.

Traumatized Mind & Body

Cleansing Reactions. In most cases of deep psychological difficulties, sufferers experience severe weakness during their initial tries of CFQ practice, due to the opening out and releasing of the problem. Some clients can hardly stand up for five minutes to practice the 7-movements. Severe weakness and numbness in the legs disables them, despite normally having no problem walking. Perseverance with a strong intention to get well will ensure that they gradually improve. After two or three weeks, they are able to exercise for as long as half-hour at a time. This means that they are also experiencing great overall improvement.

The nature of psychiatric problems is such that compulsive and recurrent thought patterns cause internal exhaustion, weakness, and staleness in the mind, emotion, and spirit. When these are cleared out in the release process, the weakness and staleness floods the whole body. Willingness to face abreactions is crucial to ensuring full recovery. Severe weaknesses may be experienced within the first three months, though they are greatly reduced after that. This also means that the presenting disorder has been reduced. However, complete eradication of the weakness may take two or three years.

Similarly, the outflow and unloading of spiritual and emotional pain from CFQ therapy, together with the muscular opening and realignment, result in the client's experiencing physical body pain, particularly around the neck and shoulders, and lower back. This will gradually dissipate through the limbs. The moving-out process might be felt as pain in the arms and legs. In the healing process, there will also be a reversal of symptoms in the form of chest congestion, headaches, dizziness, indigestion, purging, perspiration, insomnia, nightmares and other unwinding sensations.

Attempts to remain calm and peaceful without avoiding such flushing away of debased energy will bear good fruit. Dissociating from a fear of the symptoms will ensure that every bit of the problem will be fully unloaded and eliminated. At times, practitioners may also experience strong and compulsive thoughts, emotional explosions, and even temper tantrums.

Although these may be disturbing, they are part of a releasing process. A close scrutiny will reveal that they are different from the original problems. They are not deeply connected to the emotions and appear unreal or "artificial." Practitioners, who remind themselves of their responsibilities and positive values in the face of these experiences, will note that they fade away quickly. Cooperation and social support from others will help greatly.

CFQ provides training in a self-help technique to be resilient without over-reliance on professional help. CFQ reiterates the importance of a holistic approach. A holistic approach is concerned with the well being of the body, mind and spirit. The physical well being of a person is dependent on the overall well being of the whole person. By working on the whole, the unwellness or specific problem of any part has no place to hide, as the whole body is closely interconnected.

Varieties of Consciousness

I. Body Consciousness: The Five Sense Organs

The five senses are "windows" of the body with specially developed organs/faculties that provide the body feedback of its existence. These five sense organs specialize in conversion of the universe's fine cosmic energy absorbed into impressions which are registered in the remaining four levels of consciousness (mind and spirit). Thus the five levels of consciousness can be considered the life or 'spirit' of the hardware body, without which it will have no reason to live.

Energy forces so registered become stored in the consciousness as well as become condensed and absorbed into the physical body. They cause physical symptoms such as wrinkling, tissues folding and sticking, and physical deformations that inhibit the natural physiological protective functions leading to illness, disease and aging.

II. Mind (Brain) Consciousness: The Sixth Consciousness

The sixth consciousness (See Figure 13) comprises the hardware-brain which assimilates, processes, and stores information derived from the first five senses or types of consciousness. The brain is a sophisticated organic machine that operates to sort out and organize the accumulated information into memory. The natural process of thinking, visualization, and creating by the mind is using the brain or 6th sense. It is capable of continuously retrieving information from memory to react with new information, which is stored as "new" memory. It is also capable of commanding body actions and to continuously draw in cosmic energy for its functions. Any memory stored becomes permanent and indestructible.

Mental activity or the thinking process of the hardware brain creates and adds to body tension or debased energy built-up, the fundamental illness-causation agent. These stored energy forces are aroused when life experiences, events, and circumstances disturb the mind.

All energy memories are mutually connected and mutually influencing. They exist much like a ball of entangled yarn and are incorporated everywhere in the body with tendencies or inclinations according to how and where each has been created. In other words, every cell in the body is charged with information from all levels of consciousness. Each new generation of cells produced carries more memory or information than the preceding or younger generation. The added burden results in the body's deteriorating condition and further weakens its state of health with every successive generation of cells.

Figure 13
The Energy-Consciousness Connection

Energy Connection	Levels	Consciousness States
1. The Body	1st to 5th	**Sense Organs** Sight Sound Smell Touch Taste
2. The Conscious Mind	6th Consciousness	**Brain:** Perceptions Thoughts Emotions Images Memories

3   The Unconscious Mind

7th Consciousness **Unconscious States**

Mano (wu-min or dark cloud)
*Energy body of dark clouds with deep-seated memories (Ego-ignorance and confusion). These energy forces distress, weaken and age the body

8th Consciousness ***Alaya (Storehouse or Dark clouds)***
**Energy memories of white clouds or imprints (karma) condensed from lower seven levels. Seeds of future events programmed.

4. The Pure Source

9th Consciousness Eternal Light
Cosmic God-seed, Enlightened Consciousness, *Tathagata Garbha*

III. Unconscious Mind: The 7th & 8th Consciousness

Emotions are a kind of external antenna of the Mano-consciousness (similar to the Freudian and Jung Unconscious) that connects with the mind. Emotions refer to primary feelings such as fear, anger, hatred, violence, sadness, depression, worry, etc., generated from ordinary mental states and memories of experiences which become altered by the debased energy field. They exclude sublime states of tranquility, loving-kindness, compassion and true peace. These come from positive altered states filled with radiant energy that is different from the nature of one's personal mind.

Mano consciousness (called *'wu min'* in Chinese), literally means cloudy or non-transparence and is interpreted as the seat of ego and ignorance/confusion. This comes from energy forces absorbed through activation of the first six levels of consciousness. It is a form of memory with a "dumb" intelligence because it is unable to analyze information in the sophisticated way as the mind (the sixth consciousness) can.

The seventh or Mano-consciousness is a spiritual energy mass that is shaped like a irregular black cloud-like that emanates from within and protrudes out beyond the boundary of the physical body to a distance of three feet (for an average adult).

When opened out, the seemingly homogenous and shifting dark surface of the 7th Consciousness is seen as countless distinct opaque shapes, lines, folds, and colored lights with information and memories.

However, the opening-out process is complex and can only occur with a systematic technique of letting-go as taught in CFQ. In other words, the nature of this energy force becomes obvious only if "unwound," replayed, undone, or when released. Otherwise, life and traumatic experiences continue to accumulate and compact the energy mass.

The lines and folds are the basis of tension in the physical body and can be experienced, for instance, as stiffness in a person who feels unwell. Traumatic experiences fabricate more tension that seeps out from the 7th consciousness to trouble the traumatized person, e.g., nightmares, headaches, panic, paranoia, violence, and so forth.

The continuous compacting effect, as a person ages, gives rise to the wrinkles of the skin, loss of bone density or osteoporosis, loss of memory or brain cells, and deformations of the body structure all leading to deteriorating physical functioning. When a person is subjected to excessive emotional disturbance, the energy forces in the Mano-consciousness become stirred up and flow to the mind. The person becomes disorientated by this energy field and can be said to lose his or her mind temporarily.

This phenomenon happens quite commonly in the average person, but settles back soon enough. However, when subjected to extreme or prolonged excessive emotional states such as fear or trauma, a thick layer of black cloud shields the first six consciousnesses completely and refuses to settle back.

This can result in the person suffering severe psychological problems including mental breakdown, phobias, clinical depression and PTSD.

The purpose of CFQ is to clear not only the five body-senses but also to unload the debased energy burdening the subconscious 7th consciousness. As the dark energy cloud melts away, there is a seeing of "white clouds" of purer energy that is less dense but still retains a boundary.

We are moving into the fringe of the 8th or Alaya (storehouse) consciousness.

This Alaya (eight) consciousness is comprised of largely milky-colored energy forces taking on a translucent light appearance. It is the extract of the Mano consciousness but functions on its own enabling it to attract future events. All forces here are seeds that give rise to actual events in life that survives death.

IV.   The Pure Consciousness.

With further purification, the white clouds become a clear transparent film with a residual glue-like but bouncy boundary.   When this disintegrates, there appears a transparent, crystal-clear, boundless, and eternal "shining" Light.

This is called the 9th Consciousness in certain Buddhist literature.   The deepest center or core of the Alaya consciousness of "white or pure seeds" is a kind of luminous transparent light, the source of the primordial pure consciousness that illuminates the eternal Still Heart.

Accessing this light, radiating it and letting it dissolve all the created effects of life's experiences and stored memories (within the first eight levels of consciousness) to merge completely with the cosmic, eternal, transparent light remains the highest aspiration in Buddhism as well as most esoteric teachings.   This is called "emptiness", a transformation toward absolute reality.

 In CFQ practice, the cultivator clears a path of connection to this transparent light, so that it will continue to radiate out to cleanse the first eight levels of consciousness of disease-causing karmic-forming energies.

The cultivator becomes much better off health-wise to the extent of having unloaded by opening out to dissolve from within all of the body, mind, and spirit's burdens arising from previous transactions. This has to be actually done and experienced (true knowing of reality) and not just by imagining or dreaming.

The latter uses the dualistic mind's (creating, constructing, imaging, visualizing, thinking) processes that will end up increasing the dark energy cloud and thickens the Mano-consciousness.

VI. CFQ Healing.

The pure transparent light, through a long period of practice, becomes a radiant light that is uncreated and boundless. It is often tinged with a golden hue, the base light of compassion (Metta) necessary for a healer to perform healing.

The purification and radiant effect create an outpouring in the energy-consciousness aspect, opening and expanding the physical body. All disease energies are released in the process (See Figure 14).

Spirit

Refers to the non-physical life force that sustains the physical body and mind. It is the reason for the existence of the physical body and mind or the reason why a being is born. It becomes laden with the debased energy forces of memory throughout the process of life.

Empty of self but full of radiance
Letting go everything, shift to pure cosmic energy.
Abiding in the present, one is a golden Light
Eternally illuminating all.

Figure 14
Letting Go of Biopsychosocial Trauma

The greatest healer is peace

CFQ Meridian healing movements are merely tools to enable you to inculcate peace. They are necessary as without them peace can never be revealed in you. With diligent and prolonged practice, you can shift from the "I want"' state to seeing and feeling the transcendent state of peace--a magnificent reality of illumination without boundaries.

The Last Supper a.k.a. "Movement of the Minds"

Cenacolo di Leonardo da Vinci: Christ Consciousness

Part Two

Meridian Exercising

Medicine of the Heart:

Bio-energy, called qi, is the most basic function in life. When the energy sinks, hundreds of diseases disappear. A disease of the heart must be cured by "medicine of the heart." If a person is peaceful, calm and not greedy, his/her real energy is harmonious. If s/he guards the spirit against outside disturbances, disease finds no way to attack.

Book of Nei Ching

5

Practice of the Hexagram
in Seven Movements

In the hexagram dance, the yin (hollow) movements enhance the yang meridian energy flow. The yin meridian energy flow is amplified by ensuring a projection through the hands and feet with the yang (solid) movements.

There is yang within yin, yin hidden behind yang, hollow contains solid, and solid motivates hollow. This is the core philosophy of the ancient Book of Changes (I Ching): the yin yang and five elements mutually complementing and mutually contrasting, from which all changes are created. With proper use of the principle, arises the hexagram.

According to ancient beliefs, the human body is the exquisite creation of the infinite power of the universe thus enabling it to "flourish and nourish without extinction," and to "continue in perpetuity," or existence in infinite continuity.

All matter in the universe comprises, "a thousand changes and ten thousand transitions," symbolised by the hexagram. By adopting this principle in these exercises, the physiological functions of the body are brought in tune with the universal law of changes (Yap & Hiew, 2002).

Seven Dances of the Universe

Bioenergy flow is optimum when performing the exercises standing with your feet parallel one foot apart. Looseness of your body enhances energy flow, which is easily obstructed by strength. Understand the healing principles of moving. It is totally different from normal movements and exercise. The secret is to move effortlessly and without strength.

Movements are easy, loose movements that create an opening effect on the trapped energy. You move in tune with the energy flow: Too fast you are not enabling energy flow. Too slow it becomes a form of concentration–you actually block the energy flow.

Take care to be open. Move as if your limbs don't belong to you—like a flag on a pole that's hanging loose and sways with the wind. You do that in the way you raise and lower the arms and in the hand movements itself. Use just barely enough strength to lift up the hands to hang loosely.

Preparation

Purpose: This is a warm-up activity to relax the body by flushing out stale energy down to the feet.

Instructions: Stand with feet one foot apart.
1. Loosen the whole body with both hands hanging loosely at the sides.
2. Tilt the hands up, bend your knees, and sink down. This will relax the hamstring (*song-kua*) to loosen your hip and clear out stale inner strength (*fa jing*). (See photo below)
3. Shift body weight to the soles of your feet. Project stale energy out from hands downwards all the way to the soles of both feet. Feel a smooth energy flow relaxing your shoulders and entire body.
4. Positive thoughts and actions generate good energy that is essential for good health and fortune.
   Repeat 10 times.

Set-up of Hexagram Dance

The Practice: Sequence of 7-Movements

(Note: Full illustrations of the steps of each movement in next section)

Movement 1:
Flying Cloud Hands (fei yun shou)

Energy Effects:

Stimulates bioenergy flow in all the 12 major meridians as well as enhances downward flow through the hip region, flushing out stale energy thoroughly.

Health Effects:

Good for overall well-being uplifting one's spirit to replace anxiety and depression and speeds up recovery from illnesses.

Purpose:

This exercise ensures deep meridian energy flow. Raising the arms with palms hanging loosely stretches and stimulates energy flow in the 3 yang meridians. By lowering the arms and hands, they stretch and stimulate energy flow in the hands 3 yin meridians. Bending your knees slightly to loosen the "*kua*" or hamstring enhances downward energy flow. At the end point, use inner strength to exert pressure on the palms and feet. That means the entire body will be devoid of strength.

Beginning: Positioning the Feet

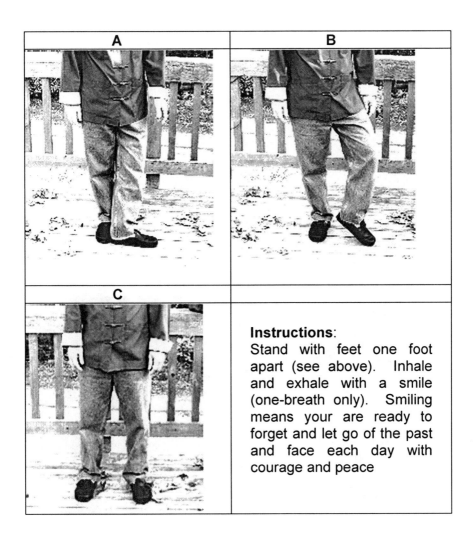

A	B
C	
	Instructions: Stand with feet one foot apart (see above). Inhale and exhale with a smile (one-breath only). Smiling means your are ready to forget and let go of the past and face each day with courage and peace

Procedure

Begin with counting 'One' and continue to smile.

Meridian Movement 1: *Flying Cloud Hands*

Step A

1. Raise both hands with arms straight to the front at below shoulder level (use minimum strength). The fingers are loose and pointed downwards.

Step B

2. Pull your hands back below your shoulders.

Continued **Meridian Movement 1**

Step C

3. Drop your hands straight down until your arms are straight.   Bend your knees to free your *"kua"* (or hamstring). Feel pressure only on the palms and feet (dynamic *song kua-fa jing*).

Step D

4. At the end, fingers should point to the front.
                                    Repeat the exercise ten times

Movement 2:

Touching the Jade Belt (*mo you dai*)

Energy Effects:

Clears out stale energy in the hands 3 yin meridians exchanging with cosmic energy that flows back through the hands yang meridians. Also relaxes the belt meridian and flushes stale energy down from the waist to the feet.

Health Effects:

This exercise helps to cope with indigestion, over-weight problems, gout, postpartum depression, back pain, and sciatica. It stimulates healthy functioning of organs to prevent: ovarian and prostate problems, urinary and kidney disorders.

Purpose:

Sends the energy out through the hands 3 yin meridians. Exchanges the stale energy with pure energy, at the same time energising the lower abdomen. Relaxes and activates energy flow in the belt meridian. Finally, loosens and expels tension energy all the way down. Apply inner strength where muscle exertion is required.

Procedure

Position your feet one-foot apart and count 'One':

Meridian Movement 2: *Touching the Jade Belt*

Step A

1. Raise both hands to the navel level at the sides of your body.

Continue *Touching the Jade Belt*

Step B

2. Extend the hands forward. Open out the fingers using minimum strength. Take note of the contact under the feet to prevent an upsurge of energy. The latter is due to opening the fingers with palms faced up.

Continued **Meridian Movement 2**

Step C

3. Turn your palms over facing downward with fingers hanging loosely.

Step D

4. Bring your hands back toward your navel. Move your hands across until they reach the sides of your body. Turn the palms downward and move down at the same time bending your knees (dynamic *song kua-fa jing*).

Repeat 10 times, counting each time

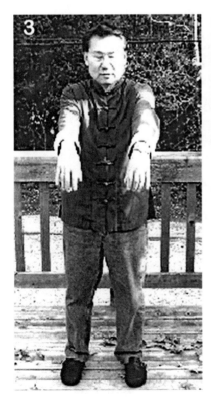

Movement 3:
Happy Heaven, Happy Earth (huan tian xi ti)

Energy Effects:

Opens out the whole body's bioenergy system to enable free exchange with the cosmic source. Facilitates yang energy flow together with *tu* energy meridian at the back of the torso. Also yin energy flow together with *jen* meridian in the front torso. Enhances equilibrium and harmony of the body's energy system.

Health Effects:

Overall, the head region and internal organs are cleansed to clear out dizziness, fatigue, numbness, insomnia and indigestion. Blood flow is enhanced to cope better with diabetes, arthritis, heart ailments, and the immune system is enhanced to promote recovery from chronic problems.

Purpose:

This exercise is to link and harmonise the upper with the lower body and to connect all meridians from hands to feet enhancing the whole body exchange with cosmic energy. The motion also stimulates energy flow in the back *tu* meridian. The above cleanses the head (eyes, ears, nose, throat) the internal organs, and stimulates energy flow in the front *jen* meridian. The feet 3 yin meridians are cleared and energy flow in the feet 3 yang meridians is stimulated. Overall, it enhances wholeness and harmony of the energy system.

Procedure

Stand with feet one foot apart and count 'One'

Meridian Movement 3: Happy Heaven, Happy Earth

Step A

1. Raise the hands straight up from your sides.

Step B

2. Let both palms touch above the head. Push slightly on the hands and straighten arms over the head. Take note of the contact under your feet (to equalise and prevent an energy upsurge).

Continue *Happy Heaven Happy Earth*

Step C

3. Move your pressed hands down the front of your forehead and turn the palms inward opening them toward your face.

Step D

4. Continue to move the arms in unison downward with palms facing chest and stopping at the lower abdomen.

Continue Happy Heaven Happy Earth

Step E

5. Drop both hands straight down in the centre of the body until both elbows are straight. At the same time bend the knees slightly *(song kua)*. Spread your arms straight out until wider than the position of your knees. Arch the hands *(fa jing)*. Return to hip level and straighten the legs at the same time.

Repeat (1) above and begin with dropping both hands straight down to the sides while maintaining the straightness of the knees.

Repeat 10 times (Steps 1-5), counting each time.

Movement 4:
Oh My Precious (xin gan bao hei)

Energy Effects:

A wonderful relaxation exercise to thoroughly loosen hip and lower back and enhances *qi* blood supply and circulation to the internal organs.

Health Effects:

It improves nervous system functioning and immune systems to clear chronic infections in the chest and abdomen. The activated energy and smooth flow treats problems such as anxiety, depression, memory loss, and the diseases of ageing.

Purpose:

This movement especially stimulates energy flow to specific hard-to-reach or hidden areas since clearing the main meridians of the torso is not sufficient for thorough cleansing.

Procedure

Begin with feet one foot apart and count 'One':

Meridian Movement 4: *Oh My Precious*

Step A

1. Place your left hand below your chin with palm downward and right hand above your groin palm upward (energy ball). Spread the feet so that their inner sides are at shoulder width with toes pointing slightly outward.

Step B

2. Turn your body to the left and move the hands to the left side. Bend your left leg to shift the body weight on it (*song kua*)

Continue *Oh My Precious*

Step C

3. Stop the movement of the lower right hand and continue movement of the upper left hand.

Step D

4. Lower or drop your left hand (45 degrees down) and then arch the palm.

Continue *Oh My Precious*

Step E

5. Switching position with your right hand on top.

Step F

6. Move across to the right and repeat similar movements.

Continue with your right hand below the chin and follow the above procedure, turning to the right fa-jing side.

Repeat the steps as above 10 times each on left and right sides

Movement 5:
No Strings Attached (wu qian wu gua)

Energy Effects:

Covers 'hidden areas" in the body where noxious energy hides.

Health Effects:

This exercise releases the trapped energy in the hard to reach tension spots promoting blood flow and flexibility to strengthen joints, muscles, and the internal organs.

Purpose:

The gentle stretching distributes the pressure to the palms and under the feet. This has the effect of moving out stale energy trapped in hidden areas of the body–the front, stomach, and back. Be sure not to use any strength when moving your hands.

Procedure

Start:

Position feet so that their inner sides are at shoulder width.

Meridian Movement 5: *No Strings Attached*

Step A
1. Place the left hand across and below your chin with palm downward and right hand above your groin palm upward (as in Movement 4).

Step B
2. Turn your left upper hand outward and upward.

Continue *No Strings Attached*

Step C

3. Sweep right hand down besides right hip. Push both hands slightly to straighten arms.

Step D

4. Bring both hands in a tai-chi circle to shoulder level.

Continue *No Strings Attached*

Step E
5. Bend elbows with hands relaxed and fingers hanging loosely.

Step F
6. Straighten both arms sideways and turn the fingers up. Stretch the fingers and ground the feet *(fa jing)*. Return your hands to the front of your body. The hands are the reversed of the starting position (right hand up).

Follow the same movements to the right side (Steps 1-6)

Repeat 10 times each on left and right sides.

Movement 6:
Prosperity, Happiness, Longevity *(fu du sou)*

Energy Effects:

Further relaxes and frees the main hard-to-access energy blockages from head to feet to ensure smooth energy flow and flexibility in the whole body.

Health Effects:

There is a freeing effect on the back-line yang meridian *(tu)* that can trigger a chain effect to activate all the foot and hand yang meridians. Tension accumulating in the forehead is released opening the front-line yin meridian *(jen)* for energy flow.

Purpose:

This movement stretches and loosens further the most stubborn areas–the head, the back, centre of both arms and joints of both legs. The movements generate some strength that must be released through the feet.

Procedure

Stand with feet as in Movement 5, count "One."

Meridian Movement 6: Happiness

Step A
1. The feet are firmly planted on the ground entirely in this exercise.

Step B
2. Extend both arms out and bend your body to sweep forward in a 'hugging' action.

Continue *Happiness Prosperity Longevity*

Step C
3. Move the arms upward and backward toward your forehead.   Look up as you sweep your hands backward.

Step D
4. As you straighten the body, the hands are swept downward.   Knees are bent forward and backward together with the body motion.

Continue *Happiness Prosperity Longevity*

Step E
5. Follow the above with arms sweeping straight out (shoulder level) and a hug just below the throat region.

Step F
6. Follow with arms sweeping downward (toward ground) and hug below your lower abdomen.

End with arms dropping to the sides. Feel the connection of the feet on the ground.

Repeat five times (Steps 1-6)

Movement 7:
The Universe's Gift of Gold *(tian chi huang jin)*

Complete Effects:

Connects all the previous six exercises to totally flush down and expel all disease-causing tension energies. The completed sequence of the 7-movement protocols creates a perfectly smooth energy and blood flow.

Purpose:

This final movement recapitulates and connects all the above steps and further relaxes and stretches the back and legs. Similar to earlier movements, this step helps a person to be more grounded while further stretching the back and loosening the entire body. Ensure that minimal strength is used at all times.

Procedure

Position your feet as in previous movement and count "One"

Meridian Movement 7: Gift of Gold

Step A
1. Cross your fingers locking them in front of your lower abdomen. Bend your knees in a "horse-riding" stance (take care not to use too much strength).

Step B
2. Raise your hands to shoulder level below the chin. Continue in an upward motion, turning the hands outward and upward. At the same time, straighten your legs.

Continue *Gift of Gold*

Step C

3. Turn your head to look upward at your hands. Bring your awareness down to the feet as well.

Step D

4. Bend forward and downward until your hands face the ground.

Continue *Gift of Gold*

Step E
5. Turn your palms up and move your hands in a scooping action. At the same time bend your knees in riding stance.

Step F
6. Stretch your hands to the sides in a pulling action. Return to the finger-locking position.

Hexagram Ending: Affirmations

Effects: Positive affirmations that harness healing energy to amplify the beneficial effects of the exercises.

Affirmation Instructions:

Position your feet close together with heels touching.

Clasp your hands on the Palace of Life (lower abdomen) and extend the affirmations to the Universe

Continue *Ending Affirmations*

Say to yourself:

My blood and qi are flowing smoothly (and beautifully)
I am filled with peace and joy
I am free of pain and illnesses
I am blessed with good fortune

*Repeat 3 times (*The "I" here refers to the universal "I")

Note. When performing healing exercise on behalf of someone, use the same affirmation. The "I" is naturally extended to include that other person.

Conclusion: Resilient Breathing

Effects:

Regulates your breathing with a smile to complete the energy exercises. You are freed from the energy burden.

Instructions
Position feet with heels touching.

Step A
1. Hold the hands palm upwards, one hand resting on the other.

Step B
2. Inhale and move hands up centre line of the body until the shoulder level.

Continue *Resilient Breathing*

Step C

3. Exhale, turn your palms downward and move your arms down until they are straight. (Exhale with a smile).

Step D

4. Inhale, spread and move your hands up the sides. Arms are straight and palms down until parallel to your shoulders.

Continue *Resilient Breathing*

Step E
5. Move across the front toward the area below your chin. The tips of the fingers point toward each other.

Step F
6. Move downward to straighten the arms.

Repeat three times

6

Complementary Meridian Techniques

Sit, Walk, Stand & Heal Meridian Exercises

The hexagram movements described in Chapter 5 are diversified using the three supplementary meridian exercises: Lotus Walk, Butterfly Shake and Grounding Qi. Two additional exercises, Freedom Hands and Freedom Walk are included as optional exercises.

Each meridian exercise can be used separately or practised in conjunction with each other. The choice of which to use depends on such factors as time constraints, the health problem worked on, the physical limitations of the practitioner, age, and so forth.

A program of exercises can be customised according to the needs of the practitioner. These exercises are also useful for clearing trauma in children and for balanced meridian development.

Effectiveness comes from prolonged practice. The *"lotus walkers"* and energy *"butterfly sitters"* can help themselves to heal. If they have used these meridian techniques successfully, they can be equally effective to heal others in the same manner. For those with family members and close friends that need healing urgently, they can dedicate the benefits to them. Perform the meridian exercises and extend the healing energy. The recipient need not be present or be informed of their healing efforts.

Even for those who are not about to help others with CFQ, practice it as a form of self-protection. Disease energy exists and exchanges freely between people in the context of normal care giving and handling, touch, proximity or sight. This is a source for burnt-out for personnel in the helping professions or workplaces.

Also, the mental agony of thinking or worrying about the illness and potential loss of loved ones is counter-productive and may cause health problems for helpers.

By practicing CFQ, any disease-making energy absorbed or mental stress fabricated can be readily cleansed. In healing, the practitioner does two sets of the hexagram for oneself and two sets dedicated to others. The helper can also sit down to do the butterfly shake as well.

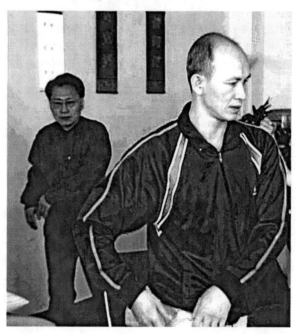

Meridian Sitting: CFQ ^{Butterfly Shake}

Objective

The *"Butterfly Shake"* is an excellent relaxing exercise for all and also appropriate for those who may be weak and frail and can hardly do any exercise. The leg movements create a downward process in line with the disease-curing path in TCM. Simplicity in performing this exercise does not diminish its potency. It provides sufficient activation to the whole body, dilutes the gripping-binding force of diseases and freeing the afflicted of such problems.

For those unable to stand or walk or engage in proper activities, time may be spent in idle thinking, self-pity, and feeling helpless which intensifies their suffering. It is also not a good idea to spend too much time on activities requiring excessive mental or brain usage, for example, reading, watching TV, and playing chess. These are precisely the main source contributing to not getting well.

CFQ ^{Butterfly Shake}

Instructions
Step A
1. Sit on a reclining chair with a headrest for maximum whole-body looseness.

Step B
2. Place the feet on the ground a foot apart and shake loosely and continuously at the rate of 60-100 repetitions per minute. *You are a butterfly perched on a blossom, happily enjoying its meal of nectar while opening and closing its wings slowly.*

Continue **Butterfly Shake**

Step C

3. Both knees should be drawn inward and outward generously. At the same time allow the movement to spread throughout the legs all the way down to your feet.

Butterfly Shake:

*Drop the mind's fabrications
that abuses
Brain-and-brawn use*

Meridian Walking: CFQ ^Lotus Walk

Objective

The Lotus Walk is precisely about non-doing. Do nothing, have nothing in mind–just walk and be peaceful! Peace and joy will only come about when a person has nothing else on the mind. But a normal person has too much of everything. To help you to be emptied bring your awareness under the feet.

Walk quite briskly yet relaxed, and be aware of the sensation under your feet when contacting the ground with each step. In this way, you switch off the thinking mind to claim your well being.

"When bioenergy sinks down, hundreds of diseases disappear."

CFQ ^{Lotus Walk}

Instructions

Step A
1. Stand in a relaxed and grounded posture.

Step B
2. Walk loosely and be aware of the sensation under your feet when contacting the ground with each step. Take care not to exert any strength or try to increase the firmness of contact by pushing your feet down.

Step C
3. Walk real easy without the exertion of normal walking. This way, the whole body is relaxed.

The unwinding of tension may lead to walking movements with a funny walk, clumsiness, etc. and sometimes it looks pretty uncoordinated.

Continue **Lotus Walk**

Do not purposefully swing your arms but let them move naturally. The arms hang loose, your steps are small and the feet are raised lower than normal waking.

The whole body should be loose and easy at the speed of a slow stroll, while maintaining a peaceful composure.

It may turn into walking with spontaneous movements of arms and the whole body. Unload strength, tension, stiffness, and whatever is released naturally.

Above all, do not lose your desire to walk everyday. I walk myself into a state of wellbeing and walk away from every illness. I have walked myself into my best thoughts and I know of no thought so burdensome that I cannot walk away from it.
Kierkegaard

Meridian Exercise: Grounding Qi

Purpose and Effects:

An extremely relaxing exercise that is highly effective in bringing the consciousness down all the way through the legs. It can be repeated in a circular motion without giving the mind the chance to stray away.

It activates and clears the qi flow in the belt meridian and the major meridians along the legs, making the whole section down from the lower abdomen completely relaxed and energetically vibrant. As a result the energy system of the whole body becomes highly vibrant.

This Meridian Exercise is effective for general healing and particularly good for arthritis, joint pains and weakness of the lower limbs.

Repeat by alternating between the left and right sides for duration of half hour. More if you wish to make good use of this exercise.

Procedure

Stand with both feet in contact at the heels, feet at 45 degrees outward, and both hands one on top of the other touching the lower abdomen.

Grounding Qi

Step A
1. Bring your mind down under your feet in order to disable the thoughts and shift to a clear and restful mind. Remain in this position for 10 seconds to a minute.

Step B
2. Bent your knees slightly ready for the next step.

Continue **Grounding Qi**

Step C
3. Move both hands to the right hip with the tips of thumbs and index fingers of one hand in contact against the fingers in the other hand.

Step D
4. Step forward with your left foot. Move your hands in a circle toward the left

Continue **Grounding Qi**

Step E
5. Continue the circle until it ends the left hip

Step F
6. Then return to the right hip by bringing it across the lower abdomen against the belt meridian.

Repeat for 50 or 100 repetitions at the rate of five to eight minutes per 100 repetitions.

Continue **Grounding Qi**

Step G.
7. Change sides when the hands are at the side of the left hip by pulling back the left foot. Bend both knees and step the right foot forward.

Step H
8. Both feet should be positioned at shoulder width with the left front heel on the same line as the toes of the right hind foot.

Continue to circle your arms and rest on the right hip. Then return to the left hip by bringing it across the lower abdomen against the belt meridian

Repeat for 50 or 100 repetitions at the rate of five to eight minutes per 100 repetitions.

Meridian Standing: CFQ ^{Freedom Hands}

Objectives

Freedom Hands is an instant energizing exercise that provides a quick loosening, relaxing and freshening effect within a short time (of say three to five minutes).

It is very beneficial if performed during short breaks from work. It also helps to check whether you are adequately loose or slow when performing the movements.

Strength will be trapped in the joints causing pain if the movements are too fast or over exertion. It is a useful warm-up step before CFQ exercise or meditation to prepare the body for more effective practice.

Instructions:
Spread your feet about shoulder width and relax the whole body.

CFQ ^{Freedom Hands}

Step A
1. Lift your right arm straight up to the front until slightly below your shoulder level with the hand hanging down loosely and bend your right knee at the same time.

Step B
2. Bend the right arm to pull back the hand beside your right chest. Then straighten the right arm downward with the palm facing the ground. (*song kua & fa jing*).

Continue **Freedom Hands**

Step C
3. At the same time raise the left arm up front, bent the
    left knee and shift your weight to the left.

Step D
4. Pull back on the left arm and straighten the left knee.

Alternate between the left and right side with a continuous
movement.

Performing 15 repetitions should take one minute's time.

Meridian Stepping: CFQ Freedom Walk

Objectives

Freedom Walk is similar to the above except that it becomes a walk. It also gives a better sense of freedom if done by walking outdoors or a wide-open space. However, as the way you walk may look strange to passers-by, some of you may not wish to be seen walking in this way.

This step helps to improve your sense of balance, enhances the grounding effect to bring about faster recovery from diseases, and increases the flexibility and strength of the lower limbs.

Ensure that you do not exert strength on your legs or hands when performing the Freedom Walk.

Procedure

Move your hands similar to the "Freedom Hands" movement except that when you lift the hands to the front, you step forward using the alternate leg.

Step A
1 Lift your right arm straight up to the front until slightly below the shoulder level and left leg in front. The right hands hang down loosely, and bend your knee at the same time.

CFQ ^{Freedom Walk}

Step B

2   Without moving the legs, pull back right hand to side of chest. Move the right hand down with the palm facing the ground and raise the left arm stepping forward at the same time with the right foot.

Both legs are neither deliberately bent nor straight. The whole body is as loose and as natural as possible— almost like normal walking except slowed down. This is to allow time for the hand to move since there is a longer distance and also to follow the timing of energy flow.

Continue **Freedom Walk**

Step C

3   Right leg in front when doing this movement: Lift your left arm straight up to the front until slightly below the shoulder level, with your left hand hanging loosely bending the knee at the same time.

Step D

4   Continue to walk forward in a similar manner. Take care not to exert force throughout.

CFQ Meridian Therapy

Psychological and biological problems can be healed by direct CFQ energy transmission, which dissolves and unloads fundamental causes. However, clients often have finicky and suspicious minds, and lack perseverance. They may stop coming for treatments even though improvements are noticeable. Their paranoia may make them speculate negatively about pain and discomfort. These responses further aggravate the discomfort in the cleansing process, making successful and satisfactory healing difficult.

The crucial criterion is whether the individuals are truly sincere in wanting to get over their problems. With such sincerity, proper cooperation, mutual feedback and counseling it is possible to overcome the problem. For those who genuinely wish to get over their problems, and if the mental disturbance evolves around specific issues, CFQ healing offers a way to quickly eliminate the disturbance.

This technique can successfully rid clients of psychosocial trauma, shortness of breath, job anxiety, allergic reactions to smoke, and fear of losing control.

It is also effective for most cases where specific psychosocial fears or traumas can be easily identified. In all cases, successful treatment is dependent on a genuine and sincere desire of the client to overcome the problem (See Diagram 1).

Diagram 1
Mind-Body & Energy Flow Methods of Destressing

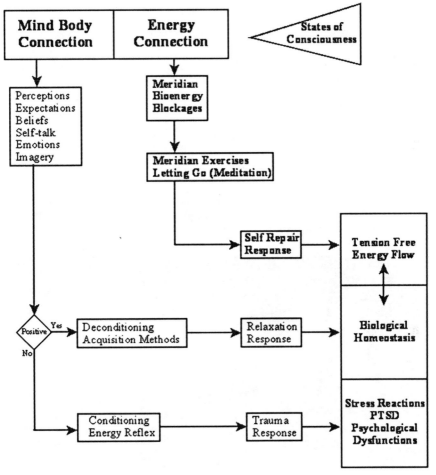

Energy Psychology

Instructions

1. Ask the person to think deeply on the problem, to activate and arouse the energy involving this matter.

2. Get the clients to note the degree of perturbation using a SUD scale (Subjective Unit of Distress scaled from 0 to 10).

3. Ask the client to say aloud the following affirmation: *"Even though I have problems and faults, I deeply and completely accept myself."* (Repeat three times).

4. Allow the client's eyes to close to relax while the caregiver becomes sensitive to the tension spots of the energy pattern.

5. Undo the energy problem by tapping, slapping, massage and plucking off (done on or shown to client). In general, it is helpful to gently tap the whole scalp, rub the forehead and eyebrows in an outward direction from the center. Also massage the neck and shoulder out through the hands in a soothing manner. Finally massage the back and slap down gently all the way to the legs and feet. This process can last about ten minutes (If touch is not appropriate show the client to do self-massage).

6. Ask the client to think deeply about the problem again, to note its perturbation level. (In a successful treatment, the thoughts cannot readily be formed and neither do they cause any emotional arousal.

7. If the client rating is '0' the problem is cleared for good. (In most cases, the problem is reduced to 2 and 5).

8. Investigate whether the client has other, related issues that are disturbing, and repeat the above procedure (In most cases, some related problems will be presented).

9. When they clear off, all will be reduced to 0. In a successful treatment, a half hour session often eliminates the problem. Otherwise, repeat the procedure for several sessions.

10. A client healed in this way should be encouraged to practice CFQ (particularly the 7-Movement exercises) to further relax. This is to change the physiological structure and reduce development of future psychological problems. Otherwise, the client's physical, emotional and energy patterns may still be prone to such problems.

Figure 15
Butterfly Meditation Exercise

Healing's just another word
For nothing left to do

7

Energy Meditation Exercises

This is a mind-in-body intervention aimed at enhancing on-going practice to sustain energy flow along major meridians. Each meridian movement (Movements 1, 2, 3, 4) can be practiced as a form of energy meditation. When repeated over several hundred times (from 200-500 for 30-45 minutes duration) each meridian exercise creates wide-open meridian channels conducive for rapid healing and prevention of disease problems.

It overcomes the following setbacks faced by conventional meditation:

i.   Keeping the body still does not facilitate energy and blood flow. Thus the health benefits are doubtful;

ii.   Need to visualize-concentrate as this does not effectively enhance relaxation;

iii.   Obstruction of energy and blood flow due to certain posture (e.g., the cross-legged position).

iv.   The inability to sustain stress reduction, genuine relaxation and the healing mechanism.

Meditation Exercise Benefits:

(A). Good relaxation is one benefit: Exercising without strain drains the mind of anxiety and enhances the physical body's repair mechanism by improving blood circulation, the immune system and nerves impulses. Exercising in this manner is in accordance with what the Ancients (traced back 6,000 years) practiced as true exercise for health (See Figure 15).

A normal exercise, as most people know today is considered as *"burning away one's life."* To move in this manner sends a clear and strong message to the muscles and organs to be actively healthy. It improves blood circulation (the yin element) by enhancing energy flow (the yang element). (Strenuous exercises on the other hand stress the body and heart leaving behind a harmful residue from strain and exertion).

(B). It is also a better way for weight reduction by improving the drainage and waste removal system without the need for vigorous "sweat and burn" exercising.

These meridian exercises are also age-friendly and can be practiced throughout the lifespan as most physical exercises have to be curtailed with aging due to physical inability. Such a curtailment shatters self-confidence resulting in further deterioration in health.

(C). With the body relaxed and mental activities reduced, consciousness is no longer confined to stress-provoking thoughts and states within the physical body.

The occurrence of Stillness results in an expansion of consciousness together with paranormal visions and sensations. It paves the way for spiritual development. The meditation exercise facilitates spiritual understanding and development in the context of one's own faith.

After practicing 1 or 2 sets of the Hexagram Dance, proceed with the following steps repetitively ending with affirmations and resilient breathing.

Meditation Exercises

Each of the energy motions (M1 to M4) can be practiced in turn for a period of 3 months.

After that, each movement should be repeated for a second round for a period of 6 months.

Practice daily the movement for 1 hour and take care to count each repetition.

Procedure

Begin with Movement 1 (Flying Cloud Hands) as the first form of energy meditation.

1. Count each repetition to bring the mind to the present and to be more aware of the body's energies.
2. Repeat the movement 300 times at the start and when comfortable extend the practice to 500 repetitions (duration 45 minutes).
3. Conclude with affirmations and resilient breathing. Each of the energy motions (see below for the 4 movements) is to be practiced, in turn, for a period of 3 months. This becomes a 12 month long program.

Meditation Movement 1
(Flying Cloud Hands)

Energy Meditation: Do 500/600 repetitions
(40 to 45 minutes)

Continue **Meditation Flying Cloud Hands**

Energy Meditation Effects

Experience:
An expanded consciousness
Deep relaxation and Stillness
The seeing-feeling of disease problems in the form of clouds, images or heaviness.

Meditation Movement 2
(Touching the Jade Belt)

Energy Meditation: Do 200 repetitions
(40 to 45 minutes)

Continue **Meditation Touching Jade Belt**

Energy Meditation Effects:

Experience:
Seeing light and their movements.
May also see through one's own body and the organs within.

Meditation Movement 3
Happy Heaven, Happy Earth

Energy Meditation: Do 200 repetitions
(40 minutes)

Continue **Meditation Happy Heaven Earth**

Energy Meditation Effects

Experience:
Further develops seeing one's transparent body
May experience a kind of light-existence or consciousness without body.

Meditation Movement 4
(O My Precious)

**Energy Meditation: Do 250 repetitions
(45 to 55 minutes)**

Continue Meditation Oh My Precious

Energy Meditation Effects

Experience:
Clearer expansion of consciousness and
a sense of existence with a consciousness completely
independent or detached from the body.

Self-Evaluation

This self-regulation technique is mastered when you are able to sustain practice of any one of the movements (M1 to M4) continuously for a period of one hour without difficulty.

Obstacles to Practice

1. The mechanical and repetitive nature of such an exercise directly challenges the desire-mind, which has been programmed for thrills, and excitement that directly produces non-stop karmic creation of problems including disease.
2. Such a challenge readily manifests as boredom and reluctance to continue with the meditation exercise. Readiness and willingness to face and overcome boredom reveals peace, which arises from non-desire, non-attachment and is void of excitements.
3. Peace is not only the healing resource par excellence but approaches and touches the profound transparent radiance of Emptiness that assured spiritual evolution.
4. The enormous amount of accumulated stale energy that is removed (karmic cleansing) gives rise (from mild to severe) numbness of the lower limbs which can be challenging especially during the first few months.
5. This can be agonizing but is also evidence of the benefit of the meditation exercise to clear off the numbness left within the body in the non-dissolved state. Imagine the harm and damage it would cause to body and bodily functioning.
6. It can be a time bomb with the eventual force of death. Its removal means rescuing the person, storing the self-repair functions and the extension of one's lifespan.

Direct Energy Transmission

A meditation method that can also be used for healing is described *(See Meditation Healing Guidebook, CFQ Course Level II).* This is a "direct energy transmission" form of traditional healing in a meditative healing state (Yap & Hiew, 2002). This technique is for those who wish to pursue a calling in energy healing as a profession. Only those with a genuine concern and interest in humanity should consider becoming energy healers. Healing should be taken as a pursuit both to help people and to facilitate understanding human behavior.

The ultimate goal is to improve one's own self-cultivation, which eventually leads to the *"illumination of the Heart."*

Healing with energy involves a heavy involvement and interference with other people's karma. The best way to ensure that this does not bring serious repercussions to oneself is to optimize the healer's purity of motive.

The advanced practitioner can also teach CFQ meridian healing techniques to those who need healing and to speed up recovery as well as provide a form of post-treatment maintenance (Figure 16).

Figure 16
Meditation Therapy

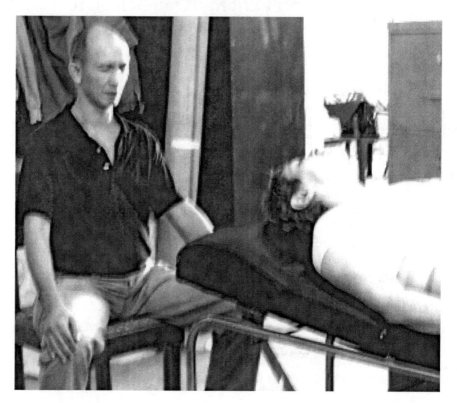

Tune in:
     To CFQ meridian cleansing
Turn on:
     Your resilient Light
Drop out:
     Noxious energy burdening body and mind
Undo:
     Antecedent cause of confusion, pain and
     illness

Healing Hands

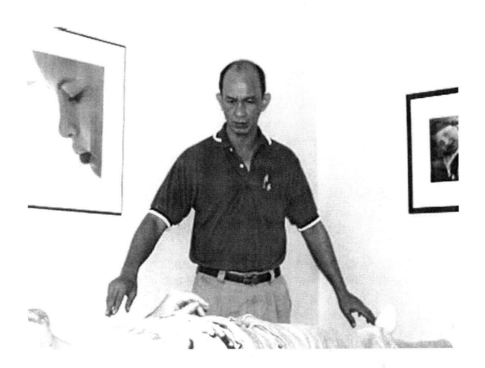

Initially, the novice healer relies on much spontaneous "doing" with healing hands by using massage, acupressure, tapping and sweeping and always with complete reliance on the golden Light or Mantra of Compassionate Love. With experience, this will gradually settle down into a kind of meditative healing where the healing energy comes out as a boundless mass to engulf the recipient completely (See Healing Techniques Guidebook, CFQ Course Level III).

CFQ ^{Healing Experience}

To practice CFQ is to tap a wondrous energy flow and experience a relaxation energy that heals at all levels. Healing occurs when these seven principles of complete letting-go become a reality for you:

1. Detach from the mind to energetic letting go:

In moving, your mind takes "time out" from routine doing (stirring thoughts & distressed emotions) to effortless, undoing actions (letting go of tension through physical energy-motions).

2. Let go via a downward release of tension energy:

Sink and flush down the dissolved tension bioenergy and blockages, the cause of all disease of the mind and body.

3. And via an opening-out radiant process:

The thorough relaxation process loosens muscles & tissues, relaxes hypertensive blood vessels, enhances blood flow and magnifies the space between cells.

4. Melt-off the "I want" energy traps that glues tension in the body:

Debased energy glue causes illness and emotional disturbances. They arise from the mind's wanting and doing-fabricating-expecting tendencies, as well as the body's cellular metabolism and the aging process. The solidified tension energies and toxic wastes are expelled and experienced as a discomforting, sticky, and glue-like sensations and waste products. Elimination of the noxious agent results in healing.

5. Undo the tension-strength trapped in the muscles:

The tension energy trapped in the muscles is drawn-in from all-physical activity and emotional disturbances. CFQ movements, during the letting-go-releasing process dissolve this gripping and binding muscle tension. When unwound it is felt as such.

6. Enhance the smooth flow of bioenergy in the meridians:

The network of energy channels (in the hands and feet) with fluid energy is able to restore healthy physiological functions, the repair of all organs (yes, even the brain!), and the rejuvenation of the resilience spirit to heal all diseases.

7. Peace—the ocean of cosmic healing energy is experienced:

You find this peace by diminishing the confusion from one's ego-identity ("I want") to become closely connected to the source of your resilience and wisdom. You surrender to the pure Spirit rather than wanting something from the Universe.

This pure energy floods one's being and repairs and restores health. The body, mind and spirit are unburdened of disease-causing tension, disharmony, conflicts, anxiety, and harmful emotions. The *peace is a pure consciousness* that spreads out from the innermost heart to become a light, vibrant, radiant and boundless field of energy. This energy field is a vividly felt luminous state of well being—a bliss and joy that transcends ordinary consciousness.

The Benefits of CFQ ^{Meridian Healing}

Healing Effects

The benefits of CFQ exercises come from daily practice. With the energy forces evaporated, the radiant golden energy builds up a resilience that ends and transforms your healing crisis. Radiant consciousness is communicated to every cell in the body. Every part of you mentally, emotionally, and physically is radiant and glowing with health. People with few serious health problems need only to complete two or three sets of the 7-Movement protocols (about 30-45 minutes) and selected complementary exercises.

Those with health problems are recommended to do three sets augmented with complementary CFQ exercises such as lotus walk and butterfly shake (See Figure 17). In addition, each of the first four movements can be repeated as a form of meditative healing. The practice can be spread out over the day and evening. Some specific benefits:

Movement 1: Flying Cloud Hands:

For frozen shoulder, neck pain, fatigue, insomnia, migraine, tinnitus, cataracts, asthma, heart ailments, menstrual disorders, constipation, anxiety, depression, high blood pressure, diabetes, infertility, and arthritis. Also helps to improve the depressive mind-set of cancer patients to promote recovery.

Figure 17
CFQ Meridian e-Motion

Freedom Walk

Healing is another word for nothing left to lose

Movement 2: Touching the Jade Belt:

For erectile dysfunction, menopause problems, prostate problems, ovarian cysts, urinary and kidney disorders, back pain, sciatica, hemorrhoids, constipation, indigestion, post-natal disorders, obesity, and gout.

Movement 3: Happy Heaven, Happy Earth.

For diabetes, migraine, dizziness, fatigue, insomnia, tinnitis and hearing defects, cataracts, glaucoma, memory loss, frozen shoulder, gastric disorder, and arthritis.

Movement 4: Oh My Precious.

For most chronic and old-age diseases including Alzheimer, Hepatitis C, anxiety, and depression. Also helps to clear chronic infections of viral, bacterial, and fungal origins.

Movement 5: No Strings Attached.

Enhances optimum health of the internal organs and clears rheumatism, joint pains, and numbness.

Movement 6: Prosperity, Happiness, and Longevity.

For lower back pain, sciatica, spondyliasis, ovarian cysts, erectile dysfunction, infertility, obesity, digestive disorder, hepatitis, stones.

Movement 7: The Universe's Gift of Gold.

Reinforces recovery of all the above.

Part Three

The Heart of

Healing

8

Complete CFQ Practice

The Secrets of Movements

By replacing thoughts with movements, the primordial resource for thinking (life force) is returned and moves through the body to enhance healthy functioning.

Positive thinking is can be adversely helpful in healing in that it continues to rob the body of its life-sustaining energy. Furthermore, the reason for positive thinking is because there are presenting problems or anxieties, and positive thoughts serve to remind you of such problems. The anxieties can trigger negative thoughts that are even more harmful. Actions must be taken to successfully switch off any form of thoughts to arrive at positive effects.

Health enhancing or meridian movements are able to reduce tension knots and folds in the body to undo the binding strength that obstructs and constricts physiological functions. Eventually they subdue the thinking mind in order to eventually clear away anxiety, depression or compulsive thinking to eliminate the attaching nature of disease problems. The outcome is healing of disease problems, and creating an opening effect that optimizes the space within the body for healthy functions.

To enable such effects, the energy movements must be carefully designed to incorporate healing principles; otherwise no positive changes can ever take place. They are reiterated here:

A. **Loose, hollow movements**. Effortless movements eliminate the effort (strength) created by thinking, particularly anxious or negative thoughts, and trapped, pent-up strength from past thoughts and physical activities. It has a smoothening effect that removes the blockages, knots, and folds within the body.

B. **Releasing inner strength (fa jing)**. This is the cutting edge that breaks up the internal knots and folds from the depths of the body. It helps to re-structure the body for healthy functioning.

C. **Slow movements.** Movements must be at the right speed to be in line with the natural flow of bioenergy. Faster movements disharmonize the body's functions by confusing the bioenergy flow, enhancing stress and anxiety. Constrained movements (moving too slowly) restrict bioenergy flow and is equally not health enhancing.

D. **Straightness of joints**. Ensuring the straightness of joints whenever applicable in performing the exercise will prevent trapping the flow of bioenergy and reducing the effectiveness of the exercise. In particular, the joints must be relaxingly straight (see illustrations in previous section).

The knee joints are straightened after each "song kua" movement. Also:
    The elbow joints when executing "fa jing"
    The elbow joints when performing:
    Step (2) of Movement 1
    Step (2) and Step (4) of Movement 2
    Step (4) and Step (6) of Movement 3
    Step (4) of Movement 4

E. **Unplugging Bioenergy channels.** The movements in CFQ exercises are in line with the pathways for bioenergy flow, called meridians in Chinese medicine. They enable the optimum removal of blockages in the body which hinder proper physiological functions, at the same time ensure that mental attachments, anxiety and compulsive thoughts are successfully drained off. Diligent practice over a period of time results in a sustainable and improved positive outlook in life, healing resilience and desirable attitudes. Such positive effects will not take place if the bioenergy pathways are not complied with.

F. **Pausing to Prevent Energy Backflow.** Pause a second or two to switch the bioenergy flow: Practitioners should pause shortly to allow the switching of bioenergy flow between one set of meridians to the next rather than moving in a non-stop, continuous manner. Without allowing time for switch over, proper flow is hampered giving rise to disharmony. In particular,

In Movement 1, pause after Steps (1), (2) and (3)
In Movement 2, pause after (1), (2), (3), (4), (5), (6) and (7)

The same rule must also be observed when performing the other steps.

The Hexagram Dance and complementary meridian movements are completely illustrated in the next section.

Hexagram Dance: Movement 1
Flying Cloud Hands

Continue **Movement 1**

Hexagram Dance: Movement 2
Touching the Jade Belt

Continue **Movement 2**

Side View

Hexagram Dance: Movement 3
Happy Heaven Happy Earth

Continue **Movement 3**

Side View

Continue **Movement 3**

Side View

Hexagram Dance: Movement 4
Oh My Precious

Continue **Movement 4**

Hexagram Dance: Movement 5
No Strings Attached

Continue **Movement 5**

Hexagram Dance: Movement 6
Happiness, Prosperity, Longevity

Continue **Movement 6**

Hexagram Dance: Movement 7
Universe's Gift of Gold

Continue **Movement 7**

Hexagram: Conclusion
Affirmations (See next page)

Hexagram Affirmations

Feeling fully grounded,
Repeat the Affirmations 3 times

My blood and qi are flowing
smoothly and beautifully
I am filled with peace and joy
I am free of pain and illness
I am blessed with good fortune

Hexagram Dance: Conclusion
Resilient Breathing

Continue **Breathing**

Side View

Sitting Meridian Exercise: Butterfly Shake

Continue **Butterfly**

Standing Meridian Exercise: Grounding Qi

Continue **Grounding Qi (Right side)**

Continue **Grounding Qi (Left side)**

**Figure 18
Coming Home**

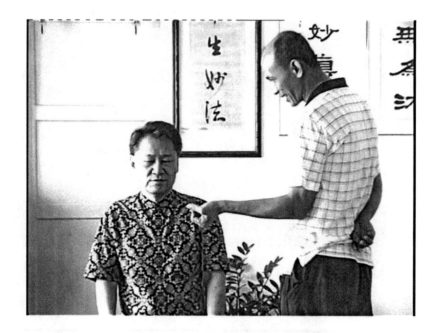

*To Play Is Human
Replay Divine
Letting go the CFQ^Way
Flows the Sublime*

9

CFQ Cultivation

The Truth about Qigong

Qigong exercises are designed to promote the smooth flow of qi or bioenergy and clear away blockages in the meridian channels, which in turn enhances blood circulation. Qi is the yang aspect of the body's essence and blood is the yin aspect. Qi flow attracts blood flow much in the same way as the positive and negative charges of a magnet), eliminates the "runaway," outstanding memory that agonizes and enslaves the mind to harmonize the mind, body and spirit, and frees off the space within the body to restore proper physiological functions. These effects can only take place by way of a letting-go/undoing approach as widely promoted in ancient, authentic teachings in Buddhism, Taoism and Chinese medicine.

Modern exercises that began gaining popularity during the past 50 years or so are largely borrowed from competitive sports. The "sweat and burn" effect was described by ancient health experts as "burning away one's own life."

Letting-go approach opposes the popular belief of empowering or strengthening qi as taught in many qigong methods. The latter does not find validity in ancient/authentic teachings but appeared widely in folk legends and side teachings. However, due to the appeal to the normal, desire-seeking mind, promises of empowerment, strengthening and absorbing are fast to receive widespread acceptance. Such teachings produce a rapid sense of "cure" but are unable to go beyond to eliminate the source of problems.

Attachment resulting from the belief in a power source called qi creates karma or memory forces that continue to fold and deform the physiological structure, aggravating disease problems in the long run.

Due to widespread popularity in the belief of empowering or strengthening/acquiring, CFQ practitioners must take care to correct their mind-set, otherwise effectiveness may be compromised.

The reason why the idea of empowering/strengthening/acquiring became so widespread is probably due to the implications suggested by the word Qigong itself. Qi is synonymous to air and a literal interpretation is how to process air to convert into the body's essence, and the more the better.

However, a less considered fact is that qi is also used to describe emotional states, which are produced by thoughts. Chinese medicine teaches about cultivating a calm and peaceful emotional state to enable a good, harmonious qi flow for optimum health. Negative emotional states produce "evil qi" that destroys the body.

Qigong truly means the art of arriving at an optimum state of relaxation where thoughts and anxiety are emptied from the mind, blockages and disharmony are completely cleared from the body, and the spirit becomes completely at peace.

In such a state, the practitioner feels a complete merging with Mother Nature, without the burden of the body and mind that feels non-existent and united to a boundless, peaceful and joyous consciousness. The closest description is "thin air." Achieving such a state or even well before that, the practitioner's disease problems and anxiety would have long vanished.

Enhancing Qi Flow

The requisite for a smooth qi flow hinges upon the following criteria:

Absence of thoughts in the mind;
Absence of physical strength in the body; and
A wide-awake consciousness.

However, it is almost an impossible feat to arrive at such a state. The mind is busy focusing on some occupation (including anxiety) or thinking randomly (as in day-dreaming) all the time. How can there be an absence of thoughts?

Thinking produces strength as verified by scientific experiments and meditation insights. The knots and folds in the body, the basis of memory, are in fact strength in condensation.

The body is completely filled up with strength. The mind together with the sense organs is busy picking up inputs at all times leaving no vacancy for the consciousness to remain independent and awake.

Fortunately there are means to arrive at such a feat. Over time, as a practitioner gets closer to his objective, they find their problems greatly reduced or eliminated. The means are through actions that incorporate features that undo the strength in the body and subdue the thinking mind.

The Re-structuring Effect

"When bioenergy settles down, hundreds of diseases disappear."

Eastern medicine discovered that the common effect of all disease problems and aging is caused by bioenergy surging up to the head and upper torso, solidifying to create stress, anxiety and agony. By eliminating/reducing the upsurge through clearing the meridian energy flow, disease problems are solved.

In esoteric teachings, humanity's nurturance comes from being rooted to Earth or nature's ground that supplies life-sustaining energy. Emphasis on material attainment and excessive quest for knowledge in modern day society makes humans ungrounded.

With a strong grounding effect, CFQ exercises not only re-connect practitioners to the ground but also bring about a sustainable and lasting change to the body's structure. Through the re-aligning of the body's musculature and organs a profound healing effect and reduction of age-related problems results. The grounding and re-structuring effects are facilitated by the use of well-balanced movements, *song kua, fa jing*, grounding qi and lotus walk.

The Non- Doing Attitude

As in ancient, esoteric teachings, CFQ exercises emphasize on the xin fa or method of the heart. It is the non-doing or "wu wei" that works!

Every thought, motivation or desire makes use of the mind and deprives the body of its life energy, creating a product called karma which stands out against the whole being. Mental activities should be curtailed in any attempt to make the body more alive (as in healing or de-stressing).

CFQ exercises replace positive thoughts with positive actions. Through the act of movements to switch off the thinking mind, life is restored into the body.

For it to be effective, one must embark on the "doing of non-doing," without which, the mind continues with its doing unceasingly. In a strict sense, the person should not even bother about healing if one is truly sincere about healing. Otherwise, the thought of healing robs the body of its spirit to oppose healing. The result of non-doing or "without" is a wide-open, boundless peace, the healing resource.

The Homeward Journey

Disease problems are characterized by an outstanding mind loaded with anxiety and agony, a suffering body burdened with pain or discomfort, and an enslaved spirit (that aspect of a person other than the physical mind and body) driven far up and hovering on top.

An effective healing process must be able to restore the spirit into the body. This can only be done through subduing the outstanding mind. By means of actions or movements, the spirit is made to realize its home and frees itself from the enslaving mind.

It becomes inspired to fight a passage home by forcing open the knots and folds that obstruct the body. It unburdens the attaching/ disharmonious memories and instructs the body to function intelligently. Finally when the spirit settles back into the body, it is "home sweet home"- profound peace (Figure 18).

A. The Uses and Abuses of Living

The demands and functions of life are such that every single life experience, thought and action leaves behind its imprints in the form of memory. Such memories take control of our minds and propel us to think and act in accordance with their demands in order to empower themselves.

Each and every of these memories claims to be "I." They vary in strength and density according to the degree of original emotional arousal and perturbance and the number of subsequent recalls/ retrievals. The stronger ones tend to be repeated more frequently and become proportionately more strengthened.

These memories are created by the faculty of mind through the sense organs by way of drawing in and debasing (varying the vibrational frequency) the pure cosmic source. They demand and inspire the growth of cells to meet their future demands, thus becoming the basis of physical body cells.

As a result the physical body becomes deformed by knots and folds on its sub-physical level. These knots and folds are bound by physical strength that compacts and stresses the body, compressing and obstructing physiological functions.

Strong or repeatedly used memories become outstanding to the point when subsequent retrievals cause agony interpreted as stress. They also obstruct physiological functions to the point of pain, discomfort or physical disease problems.

B. Healing Strategy

The functioning of each memory fighting to empower itself does not allow the mind to rest. They "burn out" the mind causing exhaustion, physical abuse, threats of disease problems, and destruction of the body from stressful information sent by the mind. Healing in the true sense can only come from switching the mind (and emotion) off in the manner taught in Qigong. Medical remedy is meant to control and manage problems or repair a physical damage, while little can be done beyond the physical or chemical level.

There is much potential in using Qigong to complement medical remedy, or in cases when medical prognosis is less than satisfactory, as the main treatment approach

The effective switching off of the thinking mind and emotions can only occur by way of taking actions, for example, through Qigong exercises. These exercises must be fully incorporated with the relevant healing features. Normal exercises may be helpful for health maintenance but are not sufficient to result in a good healing effect.

C. Winning over Mind and Emotion

In esoteric teachings, the process of taking up a battle with one's own mind was described as, "the Tao (or Way to the Truth) is the ordinary mind." It opposes the extraordinary mind filled with desires, ideas, fantasies, dreams and anxiety. This is the greatest battle, one that out-shines every challenge in life.

With every thought, emotion and action dictated by past memories and inspired by current or prevailing conditions, one becomes a complete slave to karma which governs and controls every event or incident of life. This applies even when disease befalls. Anxiety prevents recovery and causes further deterioration.

Only by means of switching out from the thinking mind that karma together with its tricks will reveal.   CFQ provides such a distinguished system with a sharp cutting edge.

When exercising, karma feels threatened and sends constant messages of boredom, anxiety, ideas, pain and agony, threats and healing recommendations.   Good!   When these mental messages appear, your job is to persist with the exercise.   The disturbance gives you the very reason to exercise: "Shut up! I am busy."   Soon it becomes eroded by your actions and consumes itself from sending these messages.   Persistence and willingness to ignore the threats and ideas of karma manifested as mental disruptions pay off.

The outcome is clear: When the voices and messages weaken, you experience healing.   You no longer remain a slave to your karma speaking through your mind, obeying helplessly to its instructions and suffering every consequence.   You become your own boss now!   Exploration of every trick of your mind is facilitated through CFQ Level 2 training (on Light Meditation), which follows Level 1 written here.

As the saying goes, *"A human's greatest enemy is oneself."*   Without skillful means, it is impossible to fight this battle.   Once equipped with such a means, the fight becomes the most worthwhile endeavor.   When there is a will, there is a way and CFQ shows the way.   If you can win over your own mind, there is no task in this world that is too difficult for you to accomplish.

The ancients have this to say, *"The toughest task/career in this world is to become a cultivator of Truth."*   Tough as it may be, to live a normal life in this highly competitive world full of uncertainties and adversities is never easy.   Since they are both difficult, why not take the challenge?   At least it is worth a try, and every effort pays off.   Karma also means justice where nothing is left out.

D. Unifying Mind, Body and Spirit

When karma is subdued, the abused thinking mind realizes that it can take a break and recuperate from wear and tear. With a restored capacity and ability, it functions optimally and is well equipped to take on the challenges of life.

Freed from the disturbance and arousal of the karma-dominated mind, the body takes a rest too. With fewer blockages, obstacles, knots and folds, aided by the newly reclaimed intelligence returned by the spirit, it regulates the body optimally to eliminate disease problems and ensure smooth physiological functions.

Now that the spirit has been rescued from the slave-master mind and unloaded its burden and agony, it is happy resting home, home at last. It has learned its lesson and avoids being lured, tricked or threatened to go out of the way to become a slave again. This is wholesomeness and unity of the mind, the body and the spirit. The Cosmic has always wanted human beings to be in this harmonious oneness.

Embracing Peace and Accepting Impermanence

In the words of the Buddha:
> *This, truly, is peace;*
> *This is sublime, that is to say,*
> *The stilling of all formations, the relinquishment of all attachment,*
> *The ending of craving, dispassion, cessation*
> *Nirvana.*

With the mind no longer "running away," a cultivator sees the tricks of every anxiety and avoids being tricked. The person observes the threat of every problem with wisdom, extinguishing the unreal, uses their skills or gets the right help to solve the remaining. The person accepts the problem and the responsibility toward solving the problem without blame or allegations. S/he realizes that it is karma that matters, meaning that if one were to embark on the appropriate action to generate good karma, few problems can exist that cannot be satisfactorily resolved. If it cannot be resolved even with positive actions, acceptance of the destiny is still the solution.

With a new found wisdom, a cultivator is able to observe their needs or desires and the thrills or enjoyment they promise. The person understands that every possession or obsession comes with a price, and is able to dispel the unnecessary, unwholesome or unworthy object or notion. The person lives life simple and easy. Enjoyment is after all a fantasy.

True enjoyment comes from the without of it. A harmonious and smoothly functioning body with a spirit happily dwelling in it ensures joy at all times without the compacting, depressing strength. A cultivator understands that since it is birth that gives life, aging, disease and death are certain. S/he sees their responsibility to take positive actions to minimize the hardship or inconvenience when faced with such threats while, at the same time accepts the rule of impermanence.

The person lives in the reality of peace, with a clear understanding of their destiny well beyond this lifespan. The person knows that God has always been taking good care of them. In old age, they never lose their mind to past memories, emotions, fantasies and unfulfilled desires, thus enjoying peace without any fear. Right up to the last moment of their life.

Peace is after all equanimity. There are no likes or dislikes, only joy in each and all moments.

CFQ Healing

The truth about disease problems is that "something in the body "and/or mind stands out causing problems or pain." That something should not be there if there is no disease problem. That outstanding thing presents itself in the mind, body and spirit. If one has been careful not to create something outstanding in the first place, it should not even be there. The truth about eliminating disease problems is therefore to let-go of them.

However, since the creation process has taken a long time, has been complicated, and the factors/forces leading to their formation are complex, the letting-go procedure is never easy. If one were to search and destroy in order to let-go, the disease victim is not truly letting-go but instead results in yet another round of creation process.

It is therefore our job to come out with such simple techniques in CFQ that summarizes the complex letting-go principles and basis to enable the reality of letting-go. It is practical and ready to use, goes beyond medical remedies that target the hardware body to cater holistically for the mind, body and spirit.

If a practitioner cares to spend time in the practice of CFQ, wellness is the expected outcome. In cases of reversible damage, given time the problem will be eliminated. In non-reversible damage, there may be partial repair or slowing down of deterioration. There will also be substantial reduction of agony and anxiety to better cope with the problem. Every fact about life is karma, including any malfunctions or problems.

Taking appropriate actions that generate positive karma can only produce the outcome of well-being, not otherwise. If the practice is ineffective, one should re-examine the principles. In particular, the person should not practice with the intention of destroying the problems. Any problem should disappear on its own without a deliberate effort.

Any diligent practitioner can by way of doing the meridian exercising, delegate the effects to another person suffering from disease problems to effect healing. A letting-go system is wide-open, influences the surrounding, and goes beyond the boundary of the physical body. The energy system of one person does not differ from that of another; the difference is the extent of blockages that cause disease problems. Likewise disease problems share common features of an outstanding and anxious mind, distressed body, and enslaved spirit hovering on its top. The downward flushing effect promoted in CFQ provides the solution.

Healing Others: To perform healing, stand at a comfortable distance (3, 5 or 10 feet depending on what the healer feels best) at the back of the healee if he is seated, or from his head if he lays down. Practice a single step (say M1) repeatedly for 15 to 30 minutes. During this process, take care to stay with the movements in order to switch off any form of thought. If thoughts about the healee's problem or condition arise, switch to the feeling of safe assurance and that he or she is well. If thoughts arises about what may help, switch off by knowing that the greatest help is the without! In that way, healthy messages become encoded in the radiant energy that erodes the disease problem.

At the end of the exercise, affirm in the normal way as your own practice. In this case, the "I" is an extended "I" that includes the healee. For those who know how to do so, do a rub down/slap down upon completion.

Absent Healing: For absent/remote healing, simply proceed with the practice in the normal way. You should not be thinking about healing somebody. That is done before you begin. Thinking about healing obstructs the healing effect. You connect by thinking deeply about the person before commencement, but drop the idea completely when you proceed.

Each time anxiety appears, assure yourself that s/he is well and does not need help or sympathy. In that way you project a healthy message across.

When Practice Should Be Temporarily Stopped: If you are faced with severe emotional disturbance due to problems or adversities in life, you may find yourself having difficulty in practice. Traumatized emotions produce compulsive thoughts to the extent of disabling CFQ practice. You should stop your practice temporarily to allow such strong emotions to past, which usually last a few days. Chronic anxiety or depression does not carry the shock of a sudden mishap or adversity, and are therefore within the ability of CFQ to remove. Resume CFQ practice as soon as possible to overcome the damage caused.

The Ethics of Living

Our life on this world is relevant and relative to every object, person, phenomenon and events occurring. Karmically speaking, we are here to do what we are expected to. As a result of our presence here, we consume resources that are otherwise meant for others. We must therefore contribute our efforts so that others are not deprived.

In making our effort to contribute, we try to give our best without concern of the rewards. If you give more than you take, karma has a way of crediting you with the surplus, and you will be rewarded sometime and somehow.

The practice of CFQ should be secondary to this rule of living. In your effort to give and contribute, your systems undergo wear and tear, and you become exhausted. You need a break or a rest. The practice of CFQ is to switch off the thinking mind for a break, repair the wear and tear, reclaim space and recharge so that you can perform better after that. Without such a practice, you will continue to abuse your thinking mind through random thoughts and physical body through destructive activities. For the average practitioner, a practice of one or two hours daily is justifiable. Enthusiasm should not override the ethics of living.

If disease problems, pain or discomfort has prevented you from full occupation, use the spare time as much as you can in CFQ practice. There are sufficient techniques here to keep you occupied for many more hours. The objective is to return you into the productive life as soon as possible.

In life-threatening disease problems, your objective should be to rid the diseases so that you can live well and longer to serve the world.

For retirees and those who are disabled in anyway, the practice is to reduce the care and resources needed for your current or expected future maintenance. When you improve, you can still take up jobs (for example, even unpaid voluntary jobs) or develop hobbies. In this way you can reduce your needs, free the resources, or even continue contributing positively to the world.

Adherence to the ethics of life justifies actions that generate good karma (to be well). It also gives rise to spiritual revelations to understand life and cope better in any condition or adversities. In the face of such a noble direction, the bad karma of diseases, problems and adversities bows and eases up its resistance.

Qigong and Meditation

While CFQ only teaches meditation proper in Level 2 (and onward) so as to give time to prepare the mind and body, practitioners are encouraged to practice the meditation exercises recommended earlier.

> *Health enhancing qigong promotes the flow of bioenergy*
> *or qi, which depends upon:*
> *Absence of thoughts in the mind*
> *Absence of physical strength in the body*
> *A wide-awake consciousness*

In order to realize these effects, actions in the form of physical exercises must be carried out (See illustrations on the Hexagram Dance and others).

In ancient times, people practiced certain exercises and contemplation techniques to cope with life, adversities and disease problems. The insights gained gave rise to civilization's social structures, languages, medicine, rituals, trades and professions. Insights about the nature and philosophy of life became the basis of Buddhism and Taoism, which also teach the means of developing such insights. These means are what we call "meditation" today. Traditionally, meditation training was preceded by the practice of some form of exercise to prepare the body. The mental, psychological and physical techniques also exist in many disciplines and professions including martial arts and Chinese medicine. These techniques are collectively called Qigong. As many forms of Qigong were not practiced for health reasons, we have to be highly selective if we wish to use Qigong for health or for overcoming disease problems.

Also, because of the difference in lifestyles, activities, and habits between the ancient and modern times, what was health-enhancing in the past need not be so today. However, certain principles and experiences of the past are extremely valuable and useful in today's context. The heritage can be incorporated for modern use, without which newly found principles may not be substantive, validated or perfected. As the saying goes, *"there must be inheritance from the past, yet there must also be new ideas for the present needs."*

Modern Qigong should be formulated based on today's needs yet contain well-tested fundamental principles. This brings out CFQ, where principles, basis and ideology are converted into actual, practical and ready-to-use procedures that materialize reality. Principles, basis and ideology taught conceptually without practical means only enter the mind to create burdens that oppose health.

Qigong as it was and as it is supposed to be includes exercises, called "dynamic Qigong" and the quiet or stillness aspect, called "quiescent Qigong" or meditation.

Qigong practices that exclude meditation lack depth. Without insights, the logical objective is to "absorb and strengthen qi power." On the other hand, most existing meditation techniques exclude exercises thus lack a body-based practice. Without the mental feeling of their body connection meditators are unaware of becoming trapped; locking their bodies, and blocking the energy channels that deprives them from the returning home of their spirit, Meditators may end up ultimately boosting ego and forgetting to open the door into the spiritual world to understand life.

A Meditation Session

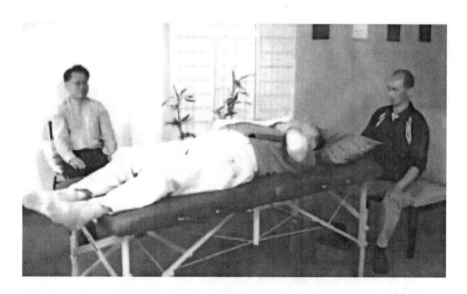

Trauma & Karma Cleansing

Figure 19
CFQ Meditation

Appendix

The healing effect of CFQ can normally be felt on the very first day of practice. However, even though every effort has been made to enable a clear understanding and effective practice, readers may not be able to practice with optimum effects merely from reading. We recommend that any enthusiastic person should receive proper instructions. A list of instructors is appended in this book.

The complete CFQ Course description is spelled out below. There are six levels of training workshops that makes up the entire course with three types of CFQ certification.

CFQ Course Description

A comprehensive energy-consciousness training and therapeutic system for healing through the removal of disharmonies which cause diseases of the mind-body-spirit and going beyond into spiritual insights and realization.

a) Provides a self-care system whereby participants are able to prevent, reduce or eliminate disease problems
b) Provides a therapeutic system for practitioners to complement existing medical treatments received
c) Provides understanding of traditional energy medicine to ensure more effectiveness for those who receive CFQ therapy or treatment
d) Provides training in healing for health professionals who wish to use CFQ energy medicine clinically and/or help family members, friends and relatives in time of need
e) Provides a spiritual healing methodology whereby participants are able to develop insights into the purpose and meaning of life under whatever faith or religion.

CFQ Training Program

The CFQ Training Course in Healing has six stages:

Level 1-Meridian Healing: Basic principles and movements
Level 2-CFQ Light Meditation
Level 3-Energy Healing Techniques
Level 4-Advanced or Refined Meditation
Level 5-Samadhi, Shunyata and Siddhis
Level 6-Toward Nirvana

Training Stages for Certification:

CFQ Instructor: Workshops at Level 1, Level 2, and Level 3
CFQ Meditation Instructor: Workshops at Level 4 and Level 5
CFQ Healing Supervisor: Workshops at Level 6

CFQ CONTACT INFORMATION

Founder
Yap Soon Yeong
15, Circular Drive,
Off Jalan Fettes,
11200 Tg. Bungah,
Penang, Malaysia.

CFQ Founding Trainer
Chok C. Hiew, Ph.D.
330 Woodbridge Street
Fredericton, NB
Canada E3B 4R5
Email: cfq@nbnet.nb.ca
CFQ Home Page: www3.nbnet.nb.ca/cfq

List of approved Level 1 Instructors

CANADA CFQ Instructors	CANADA CFQ Instructors
Dr Curtis A. Steele, MD 6095 Coburg Road #706 Halifax, NS B3H4K1 Tel:902-422-5904 Email: steele@ns.sympatico.ca	Brian Sutherland, B.Sc., PT. 18 Castleton Crescent, Dartmouth, N.S. B2X 3M3 Tel: 902-462-4157 Email:brian.s@ns.sympatico.ca
Nancy Porter-Steele, Ph.D. 6095 Coburg Road #706 Halifax, NS B3H 4K1 Tel: 902-422-5904 Email: steele@ns.sympatico.ca	Karen Whalen, Ph.D. 8 Oceanglen Lane, RR#1 Pictou, NS B0K 1H0 Tel: 902- 485-4309 Email: kwhalen@yorku.ca
Peter Goodman, MA, CTA Eastwind Health Associates 2176 Windsor St. Halifax, NS B3K 5B6 Tel: 902-422-3760 peterbgoodman@hotmail.com	Marion Stork, M.A., RPC 7008 Churchill Drive Halifax, NS B3L 3H5 Tel: 902-454-2874 marionduncan@eastlink.ca
Heidi Ship, B.A., MT 19b Idlewylde Road Halifax, NS B3N 1B8 Tel: 902-477-1409 heidiship@ns.sympatico.ca	D. Brune Clavette, DAC, RMT Talmadge Court Fredericton, NB E3B 6G4 brune@rogers.com

List of approved Level 1 Instructors

CANADA CFQ Instructors	CANADA CFQ Instructors
Dana M. Marcon 6178 Quinpool Road Halifax, NS B3L 1A3 Tel: 902-429-5214 dmtraining@eastlink.ca	Dr Perry Kent Cadegan, MD, Sterling Professional Ctr. 65 Minto St, Glace Bay, NS B1A 4R8 Tel: 902-849-3138 trancecadegan@ns.sympatico.ca
Shelley Wilcox 5 Bligh St. Dartmouth, NS B3A 1K8 Tel: 902-209-5911 shelley@TheChiStudio.com	Christine Willette 98 Lancaster Dr Dartmouth, NS B3A 4X8 Tel: 902-463-4479 jackrisk@eastlink.ca
Diane Terry, RMT 422 York Street Fredericton, NB E3B 3P7 Tel: 506-476-1515 1996@Dterry.ca	Elizabeth A. Berlasso, M.Ed., RPC, 36 Stonehaven Road Halifax, NS B3N 1G3 Tel: 902-454-6919 belasso@ns.sympathico.ca
Deborah Ann Findlay, Ph.D. 5859 Grant Street Halifax, NS B3H 3J5 Tel: 902-422-5973 debfindlay@hotmail.com	Irene Lorch-Wauchope, M.A., AT 101 Three Brooks Dr Hubley, NS B3Z 1A4 Tel: 902-876-8880 Email: irenelw@eastlink.ca
Kelly Beale 5539A Young St. Halifax, NS B3K 1Z7 (902) 488-1074 Fax 455-0006	Voni King 144 Hillside Boularderie Road Groves Point, NS B1Y 2X3 Tel: 902-544-0289

kelly@beales.ns.ca

CANADA CFQ Instructors	CANADA CFQ Instructors
Rev. Jack Risk, M.A.(SWP), M.Div ,98 Lancaster Dr Dartmouth, NS B3A 4X8 Tel: 902-463-4479 Email: jackrisk@eastlink.ca	Duncan Bremner 7008 Churchill Drive Halifax, NS B3L 3H5 Tel: 902-454-2874 marionduncan@eastlink.ca
Heather Jupp 47 Parkhill Road Halifax, NS B3P 1R4 Tel: 902-477-8697 heatherjupp@hotmail.com	Dr Christina Toplack, M.D., CCFP, 16 Main Street Wolfville, NS B4P 1C2 Tel: 902-425-4157 Email: ctoplack@eastlink.ca
Barbara Sobaskiewicz P O Box 29100 Halifax Shopping Center Halifax, NS B3L 4T8 Tel: 902-477-6474 basiasobas@yahoo.com	Anna Taylor, M.A., M.Ed. P O Box 129 Blockhouse, NS B0J 1E0 Tel: 902-624-6295 backofbeyond@auracom.com
Carl Weatherhead 1760 Cambridge Street Halifax, NS B3H 4A9	John Brennan Dartmouth, NS B3A 1K8 Tel: 902-209-5911 shelley@TheChiStudio.com
Mary Gilliss 1 Glenora Avenue Apt 1 Halifax, NS B3P 2B6 Tel: 902-477-5627 Email: gillissme@hotmail.com	

USA CFQ Instructors	Other Contacts/Organizers
Dr Patricia Fitzpatrick, Ph.D. 11755 Reservoir Road Wayland, NY 14572 Tel: 585-728-5927 Email: Psypaf@aol.com	CFQ Healing Society of Atlantic Canada Website: TBA Email: jackrisk@eastlink.ca
Scott Tate, MA, LPC, CHT 135 West Swallow B5 Fort Collins, CO 80525 Tel: 970-484-5440 Email: sstate2001@yahoo.com	**United States** Vickie Sanderson Alternatives: Ideas for Healthy Living Box 3844, Tualatin, OR 97062 Email: questions@cfqinfo.org
Dr R. John (Jack) Freese, Ph.D. P O Box 336849 Greeley, Colorado 80633-0615 Email: jfreese31@hotmail.com	Fred Nichols Ft. Collins, CO 80525 Email: fnichols@rsr.org
Barbara J. Lewis 125 Brooks Avenue Arlington, MA 02474 bjlewis@mcb.harvard.edu	
Elizabeth Bisbee 1937 Parkwild Dr #85 Council Bluffs, Iowa 51503	

Other Contacts/Organizers	Other Contacts/Organizers
Kuala Lumpur, Malaysia Richard CM Wong Suite B-19-2, Wisma Pantai No 5, Jalan 4/83A Off Jalan Pantai Baru 59200 Kuala Lumpur Email: rictec@pc.jaring.my **Singapore** Dr Joseph Guan, Ph.D Energy Psychology Centre Private Limited 2-C Jalan Pesawat Singapore 619359 Email: josguan@pacific.net.sg **Greece** Vasilis Sakkas Parados Ag.Athenasiou 4 32100 Levadia, Greece Email: sakkas@sch.gr **Portugal** Luis Morgado/ Anabela Sousa Rua Ilha Dos Amores LT-4.14.01-A, 3.ESQ Vila Expo 1990-121 Lisbon Email: lm2@clix.pt	**United Kingdom** Daniel Gumbel 3 Courtenay Road Wincester S023 7ER Email: dan.dmt@dial.pipex.com Dr Simon Phipp, Ph.D. 202 Woodstock Road Oxford 0X2 7NH Email: sj.phipp@care4free.net Ian Threadgill ianthreadgill@hotmail.com Ben Diaz Email: ben@tntdlanka.co.uk Sharon O'Boyle Castlebar Co. Mayo, Ireland oboyle_sharon@yahoo.co.uk

438775

Made in the USA